BIG BEND VISTAS

BIG BEND VISTAS

A Geological Exploration of the Big Bend

By

William MacLeod

TEXAS GEOLOGICAL PRESS
ALPINE, TEXAS

First Printing, October 2003

Printed and Bound by Capital Printing Company
Austin, Texas

Cover Photo: "Cathedral Mountain" by William MacLeod

Cover Design: Leisha Israel, Blue Sky Media
Austin, Texas

Publishers Cataloging in Publication Data
MacLeod, William
Big Bend Vistas: a geological exploration
of the Big Bend / by William MacLeod
     p.   cm.
    Includes bibliographic references and index
    ISBN 0-9727785-0-0
    1. Geology – Big Bend Region (Tex.) - Guidebook 2. Big Bend
Region (Tex.) - Geology - Guidebook.   I. Title.
QE168.B5 M24 2003
557.64-dc22

TEXAS GEOLOGICAL PRESS
P.O. Box 967
Alpine, Texas 79831
www.bigbendvistas.com

Contents

For Martha

Introduction

I wrote this book for people who want to know why the Big Bend looks the way it does. For Texans especially, and 65 per cent of visitors to Big Bend National Park are Texans, the Big Bend is bizarre, mountainous, stark, dramatic, full of exotic shapes and colors. The Big Bend is wonderful geological territory with rocks created over a very long period of time and shaped into mountains and basins by episodes of expansion and contraction of the earth's crust. Visible to the passerby as well as accessible by road, the terrain has little vegetation to obscure its natural beauty. Over a million of the four million acres covered in this book arc in Big Bend National Park and the Black Gap and Elephant Mountain Wildlife Management Areas, all open to the public by access roads and hiking trails.

I hope that readers will begin by reading the first chapter. It paints the general picture with broad strokes, introducing geological terms relevant to the Big Bend, its geological history and the factors involved in developing desert landscapes. The geologic time scale at the beginning of the chapter will familiarize the general reader with the names of the geologic periods needed in understanding the sequence of events that created the rocks and shaped the landscape.

The remainder of the book consists of descriptions of road sections, arranged into three chapters. Chapter II describes the area between Fort Stockton and the entrance to Big Bend National Park at Persimmon Gap, including the Glass Mountains and the Marathon Basin. Chapter III covers the country down by the Rio Grande south of Persimmon Gap, from Heath Canyon through the National Park to Terlingua and Lajitas. Chapter IV describes Green Valley and the southern Davis Mountains along Highway 118 from Study Butte to Alpine, and the area along Highway 67 from Alpine to Interstate 10. Each chapter begins with a geological history and map which give an overview of the area covered.

Road sections are written to stand on their own, with geological maps, cross-sections and line drawings of interesting features. Cross-references are given for landmarks discussed in more than one section. An index is also provided.

I have tried to be scientifically accurate but to avoid technical terms wherever possible. Some words have no substitutes, however, and others are useful shorthand. For these I have added a short glossary after the last road section.

I have read most of the material published on the geology of the Big Bend in the last 120 years and the material in the book has been mainly gleaned from these sources, augmented by my own observations. I do not provide citations in the text or a bibliography because it would not be appropriate in this type of book, so it is not possible to properly acknowledge my sources but most of the publications I drew on are given in the Reading List. I regret I am not able to thank them all individually but I would like to thank those who were kind enough to answer my questions in person, Daniel Barker, Thomas Lehman, William Meuhlberger and Don Parker. I would also like to thank Blaine Hall who has been enormously helpful in countless ways, especially in introducing me to developments over the past 30 years in geology and to the geology of western North America in general. Finally, I would like to thank Don and Kay Green who first brought me to the Big Bend and have been supportive in innumerable ways in the succeeding twelve years.

In a fact-filled book like this, it is inevitable that errors occur. I would be grateful if readers would write to me care of the publishers with errors they find and corrections will be made in the next edition.

I Setting the Scene

If you are traveling south to the Big Bend on Highway 385 from Fort Stockton, stop and look back as you climb up Twelve-Mile Mesa, 12 miles south of Fort Stockton. You are just east of Longitude 103° West. You will see how flat the land is to the north, a plain with scattered mesas that disappear beyond the town. If you followed the meridian north, the next mountains you would encounter would be near Karaganda in Kazakhstan, 7,000 miles away on the other side of the earth.

Mountains only form where the earth's crust buckles or where volcanoes erupt, and that has not happened between here and Karaganda in a billion years. The Big Bend, on the other hand, is where South America thrust a large section of seabed onto land, crumpling it into mountains as it did, where the earth's crust was compressed into more mountains and uplifts and then stretched to produce basins, where volcanoes erupted to create thick lava and ash beds and where enormous numbers of igneous intrusions have been uncovered by erosion, creating more mountains. The results are like nothing else in Texas.

This chapter gives some background geological information: descriptions of the rocks found, the geological time scale, how the earth's crust is structured, and an overall geological history of the Big Bend. Rocks are at the heart of any discussion of geology; they are what geologists study. In geology, a rock is any natural material, soft or hard, consisting of one or more minerals. Rocks are broadly classified into three categories, sedimentary, igneous and metamorphic rocks. Sediments are part of the cycle of nature in which rocks become exposed to the elements, water, wind, and frost, break up, and are carried down as particles into rivers, lakes or oceans, settle as layers of sediment, and over time become cemented together into sedimentary rocks. Igneous rocks are rocks that solidified from molten or partially molten magma. They can be extrusive, created on the surface of the earth, or intrusive, created underground. Metamorphic rocks are those modified by heat or pressure.

Rocks in the area covered by this book are mainly sedimentary, with scattered igneous intrusions, and along the western border of the area, a wide swathe of rocks of volcanic origin: igneous lavas and tuffs and sedimentary rocks created from reworked volcanic material.

Sedimentary rocks are mostly classified by size of the grains or clasts that make them up. The coarsest, *conglomerate*, can contain clasts ranging from large boulders to very fine-grained clay in the interstices. *Sandstone* is made up of sand-sized grains, usually of the mineral quartz, cemented together by materials such as silica (silicon dioxide), lime (calcium carbonate) and iron oxide. Rocks composed of particles finer than sand are called *shale* if they have partings and *claystone* or *mudstone* if they do not.

Limestones are sedimentary rocks composed mainly of the mineral calcite (calcium carbonate). They can be formed in a wide variety of ways. Certain kinds of miniscule plants called algae, for example, extract calcium carbonate from seawater or fresh water and create limey ooze, which eventually turns into unbedded or massive limestone. Calcium carbonate can precipitate directly from seawater and do the same. Other limestones consist mainly of fossils, shellfish remains, or coral or sponge reefs.

They sometimes contain the mineral dolomite (magnesium carbonate), which is extracted from seawater by certain organisms, and sometimes introduced by seawater after limestone has formed. If more than 10 percent of the mineral content in a rock is dolomite, the rock is called dolomitic limestone, if more than 50 percent, dolomite. Limestones containing sand or mud are called sandy limestone or marl.

Sedimentary rocks sometimes contain nodules of chert or flint. Chert or flint is composed of very fine crystals of silica, formed when silica in solution in water replaces molecules of calcium carbonate in limestone or other molecules in other rock types. Beds of chert are also common. One of the prominent beds around Marathon is a similar microcrystalline quartz rock called novaculite. Also found in Arkansas, it has been used for whetstones; the name comes from an old English term for whetstones.

An unusual type of sedimentary rock, a turbidite, is found east of Marathon. Turbidites are deposited by turbidity currents, bottom-flowing currents laden with suspended sediment that slide down sea floor slopes under gravity and deposit their loads at the slope bottoms. They can move very fast; some have been measured at speeds of up to 50 miles per hour. In turbidite beds, the coarser grained material settles out first, the finer grained material last.

Most sedimentary rocks have variations in color or grain size in vertical section, separating the rock into beds or strata, the plural of the Latin word stratum, which means something spread or laid down. Sedimentary rocks without obvious bedding are called massive.

Igneous rocks crystallize from molten rock or magma. Magma crystallizing below the earth's surface creates igneous intrusions. If it is extruded on the earth's surface, it creates volcanic lava or ash. Lavas and igneous intrusions are made up of interlocking crystals, sometimes with glass in the interstices, bound together more firmly than the grains in most sedimentary rocks. Consequently, they break down and erode more slowly than sedimentary rocks and stand up above sedimentary rocks in a region being eroded, a process called differential erosion. Volcanic ash is made up of particles of glass or pumice, glass with voids in it. It is chemically unstable and changes over time into clay creating a soft rock called tuff, a mixture of clay and glass. Tuff is easily eroded and is often redeposited as sandstone or mudstone.

Geologic Time Scale

The table on pages 12-13 gives the time scale for rocks and events in the Big Bend. Several terms used in the table are unfamiliar to the general reader, so the following sections discuss the geologic time scale and the various mechanisms that move and assemble continents and how they impact landscapes.

Geological time and the scale by which it is measured are so far out of normal human experience that they can be difficult to grasp. The scale begins with the creation of the Earth, about 4.6 billion years ago, and ends at the present day. The basic unit of time is one million years or m.y. Events are described as having occurred or taken place so many millions of years ago, abbreviated as Ma.

The earth's history is divided into eras; era boundaries are defined by events in the fossil record. At the beginning of the Paleozoic era (from the Latin for *early life*), the number of species in existence exploded and sea life developed shells that could be preserved in sediments, so large numbers of fossils began to show up in rocks. This is where the record begins in the Big Bend; no older rocks crop out in the area. The Paleozoic-Mesozoic (*early life-middle life*) boundary is marked by a massive extinction of life. Ninety to 95 per cent of marine species and perhaps 75 per cent of terrestrial species disappeared. Another mass extinction took place at the Mesozoic-Cenozoic (*middle life-recent life*) boundary, when dinosaurs disappeared and mammals took over as the dominant life form on land.

Geological Time Scale

Rocks	Period	Age m.y.	Important events in the Big Bend
Alluvium and floodplain sands and gravels.	Quaternary	.01-0	Occasional earthquakes show that Basin and Range extension continues.
Sand, pebble and boulder beds, cemented by caliche in places.	Tertiary-Pleistocene	.01-1.6	Ice ages start at beginning of period in N. USA; sea level dropped 300 feet in last ice age, which ended 8-10,000 years ago.
	Tertiary - Pliocene	5-1.6	The lower Rio Grande breaks through to connect with New Mexico and Colorado at 2.25 Ma.
Basalt flows in Black Gap; sills and dikes in National Park and west. Graben-fill sediments in Tornillo and Castolon Grabens.	Tertiary - Miocene	24-5	Basalt erupted in volume in Black Gap Graben and as dikes and sills elsewhere. Igneous activity ended about 17 Ma.
Air-fall tuffs and rhyolitic and trachytic lavas with subordinate conglomerates, sandstones, breccia and limestones created in the Davis, Chinati, Bofecillos and Chisos Mountains. Total thickness of strata up to 6,000 feet.	Tertiary-Oligocene	37-24	Period of main igneous activity with volcanic centers active in Davis and Chisos Mountains from 37 to 29 Ma. Basin and Range faulting begins in southern Big Bend at 28 Ma.
Air-fall tuffs and their derivatives develop in south Brewster and Presidio Counties and across the Rio Grande in Mexico.	Tertiary - Eocene	58-37	Volcanic ash drifts in from the south at 46 Ma. Christmas Mountains volcanic center begins erupting at 45 Ma.
Sandstone and claystone up to 900 feet thick in National Park.	Tertiary - Paleocene	65-58	Laramide Orogeny continues until 50 Ma, creating the Del Norte, Santiago and Dead Horse mountains, the Marathon Dome and the Tornillo Basin.

Boundary between Mesozoic and Cenozoic eras is about 66 million years ago.

| Marine flaggy limestone and siltstone, claystone and sandstone followed by non-marine claystone, sandstone and lignite. | Upper Cretaceous | 88-65 | Sea retreats across National Park 75 Ma never to return to Big Bend; lake and river sediments begin to be deposited in National Park. Laramide Orogeny begins 70 Ma. |

Rocks	Period	Age m.y.	Important events in the Big Bend
Cherty and shaly limestone 300 ft. thick at Hwy 90, 2,200 ft. thick at the Rio Grande.	Lower Cretaceous	144-88	By 90 Ma, all Texas under water. The Chihuahua Trough continued sinking.
Thick evaporite beds in the Chihuahua Trough.	Jurassic	208-144	Big Bend above sea level except along Rio Grande; sea began encroaching in Texas in 150 Ma. The deep Chihuahua Trough developed along the Rio Grande.
	Triassic	245-208	Big Bend above sea level except along Rio Grande.

Boundary between Paleozoic and Mesozoic eras is about 240 million years ago.

Rocks	Period	Age m.y.	Important events in the Big Bend
Limestone reefs and beds, siliceous and clay shale, chert and conglomerate in the Glass Mountains.	Permian	286-245	Permian Basin developed north of Big Bend and limestone reefs developed along margin in Glass Mountains and west.
Cambrian through Pennsylvanian sedimentary rocks, greatly crumpled and faulted, thrust onto N. America along Marathon-Ouachita Mountain range.			Thrusting of Cambrian through Pennsylvanian sedimentary rocks onto North American continent completed by end of Permian.
Sandstone, shale and limestone turbidites in Marathon area.	Pennsylvanian	320-286	Cambrian through Pennsylvanian sedimentary rocks begin to bc telescoped onto North American continent from southeast.
Shale and sandstone turbidites in Marathon area.	Mississippian	360-320	Turbid flows mainly from a landmass approaching from the south deposit sediments in a subsiding basin offshore North America.
Chert and novaculite deposited in deep sea off North American south coast tentatively identified as being Silurian-Devonian; now onshore in Marathon area.	Devonian	408-360	No record; deep sea lay off North American southeast coast.
	Silurian	438-408	No record; deep sea lay off North American southeast coast.
Cherts, shales, thin limestones deposited in deep sea off North American south coast; now onshore in Marathon area.	Ordovician	505-438	No record; deep sea lay off North American southeast coast.
Sandstone with shale layers deposited in deep sea off North American south coast; now onshore in Marathon area.	Cambrian	570-505	No record; deep sea lay off North American southeast coast.

Boundary between Precambrian and Paleozoic eras is about 570 million years ago.

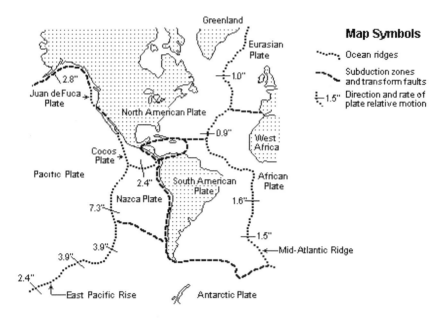

Major plates around the Americas showing directions and rates of relative movement in inches per year

Each era is divided into periods. Many of the terms come from place names, Pennsylvanian from Pennsylvania, etc. Periods are divided into epochs. In this book only Tertiary epoch names are used.

Fossils provide relative ages; to get absolute ages, scientists measure ratios of certain isotopes of elements in igneous rocks. All naturally occurring elements have one stable isotope; some have one or more unstable isotopes. Potassium, for example, has an unstable isotope, atomic weight 40 and chemical symbol K^{40} that decays into a stable isotope of argon, chemical symbol A^{40}. Igneous rocks crystallize from liquid magma and at the point of crystallizing contain no A^{40}. The rate at which K^{40} changes into A^{40} is known so the age of the rock can be calculated by measuring its K^{40}/A^{40} ratio. Another more recently developed method measures the ratios of A^{40} and A^{39} isotopes. Many thousands of K^{40}/A^{40} and some A^{40}/A^{39} determinations have gone into compiling the ages of igneous rocks in the table and the other chapters.

The Earth's Crust

The earth has a metallic core about the size of the moon, surrounded by a 1,700 mile-thick mantle of peridotite, a dark green and black rock. The mantle is mostly liquid although the lithosphere, the outer 60 miles or

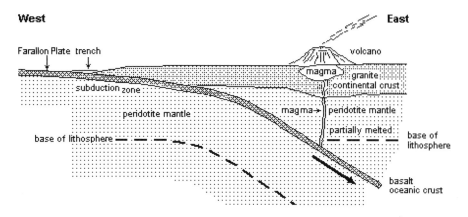

The Farallon plate is subducted under the North American continent. Volcanoes develop inland from the subduction zone in a volcanic arc.

so, is cooler than the interior and more rigid. The earth's crust, the surface part of the lithosphere, is solid. Under oceans it is up to 3 miles thick and composed mainly of basalt, a rock rich in iron and magnesium created by the partial melting of peridotite in the mantle. Continents sit in the lithosphere as islands, 20 to 45 miles thick, of mainly silica-rich rocks such as granite. Continental crust developed very early in the earth's history, most probably from partial melting of the mantle, too.

Plate Tectonics

The lithosphere is like a jigsaw puzzle, made up of irregular pieces called plates that fit tightly together. Seven are very large; others are quite small. They move around constantly, each at its own pace and in its own direction, powered by thermal currents in the mantle. Three kinds of boundaries are found between plates, transform faults, spreading centers and subduction zones. At transform faults, plates slide past each other. At spreading centers, plates move away from each other and upwelling mantle currents rise, creating ocean ridges and producing new oceanic crust continually. At subduction zones, crust disappears into the mantle, usually at about 45 degrees to the vertical, and can be traced in places as far as 500 miles below the earth's surface.

The large plates around the Americas are shown in the map opposite. The Mid-Atlantic Ridge, 6,500 feet high and 15,000 miles long and one of the largest structures on earth, bounds the North American plate on the east. On its west, a spreading center, the East Pacific Rise, had moved through time towards the continental coast. At its western boundary, the North American plate has overridden the East Pacific Rise and the Farallon plate that originally lay between the two in a subduction zone off the west coast, as shown in the cross-section on page 15. Two fragments of the Farallon plate remain, the Juan de Fuca and the Cocos plates. The East Pacific Rise now runs up the Gulf of California and turns into the San Andreas Fault, a transform fault which is active between San Diego and San Francisco. North of San Francisco, it goes out to sea again and becomes a spreading center again. Part of the original subduction zone remains between the spreading center and the coastline north of San Francisco.

Like most things in geology, plates move very slowly, about the rate your fingernails grow. Current rates range from a half-inch per year in each direction at the Mid-Atlantic ridge to over 3½ inches per year in each direction on the East Pacific Rise between the Nazca and South American plates. Relative movement on the San Andreas Fault is 2½ inches per year.

Subduction zones, in addition to consuming oceanic crust, can generate volcanic and orogenic activity (*Orogeny* means the process of building mountains). The activity depends on the types of crust that meet at the subduction zone. When oceanic crust meets oceanic crust, for example, the older and colder oceanic lithosphere sinks below the younger lithosphere, creating a deep trench and carrying basaltic crust, ocean floor sediments and seawater into the mantle in the subduction zone. A volcanic arc, a line of volcanoes, develops above the subduction zone as the cold oceanic lithosphere slab is assimilated. Lava erupted above this type of collision is commonly andesite and less commonly, basalt.

Continents make up part of the plates and move with them. When a continental margin meets an oceanic crustal plate at a subduction zone, the thinner and denser ocean plate is subducted under it, as in the Farallon plate diagram. Volcanic activity very often develops 50 miles or so inland from the subduction zone. In this case, the lava erupted above is granitic or nearly so, because it is produced from melting of the granitic continental crust. For example, in the northwestern United States and western Canada, the Juan de Fuca plate is being subducted under the over-riding North American plate today, and volcanic eruptions occur periodically in the Cascade Mountains of Oregon, Washington and British Columbia.

When a continent comes up against another continental margin at a subduction zone, mountains form. Examples include the Himalayas, which formed when the Indian plate collided with the Eurasian plate, and the Alps, which formed when the African plate collided with the Eurasian plate. Continental plate collisions are the main cause of mountain-building periods or orogenies.

Big Bend Orogenies

Two major orogenies have taken place in the Big Bend in the last 300 million years. The first occurred during the Pennsylvanian and Permian periods when the northern part of South America collided with North America in an event called the Ouachita Orogeny. It created the Ouachita-Marathon Mountains which extend from the Texas-Oklahoma border through the Marathon Basin to the Solitario near Lajitas on the Rio Grande (see map on 41). They are similar in age to the younger Appalachians and formed in a similar way. In fact, many geologists consider them to be part of the same orogeny, giving rise to the saying that the Big Bend is where the Appalachians meet the Rockies (some think that the Laramide-age mountains discussed below are an extension of the Rockies). The Ouachita Orogeny is discussed in Chapter II – The Glass Mountains & the Marathon Basin.

A second orogeny, the Laramide Orogeny, named after the Laramie Mountains in Wyoming, began on the west coast of the continent around 200 Ma and for 150 million years migrated east at 1 inch per year. As it advanced, the earth's crust was compressed, creating mountains in a zone from British Columbia in Canada to Oaxaca in southern Mexico, including the Frontal Range of the Rockies, the Sangre de Christo and Sacramento Mountains in New Mexico and the Sierra Madre Oriental in Mexico. The Big Bend is at the very eastern edge of the zone and was the last area to be affected. In it, the main Laramide mountain range runs south of the Rio Grande from El Paso to Lajitas and then turns down to become the Sierra Madre Oriental. Several mountains and uplifts were created east of the main zone, including the Del Norte, Santiago and Dead Horse Mountains, and the Marathon Dome. A basin, the Tornillo Basin, formed between the main range and the Del Norte-Dead Horse range.

After a period of inactivity, the earth's crust began to be extended or stretched from east to west creating what is called the Basin and Range province. The province runs from western Canada through the western United States to near Mexico City. The Big Bend is on the eastern margin of the province. The Rio Grande runs in an offshoot of the province, the Rio Grande Rift, from Colorado south through New Mexico to the main province at El Paso. Faulting in the Big Bend began about 28 Ma and is continuing. So far, it has stretched the earth's crust by 5 to 10 per cent across the Big Bend.

Many hypotheses have been advanced to explain the Laramide and the Basin and Range episodes. One factor that seems to be important is that North America had a now-inactive subduction zone on its west coast that consumed 8,000 miles of crust in the last 145 million years. On the east coast of North America, 1,500 miles of ocean crust were created at the

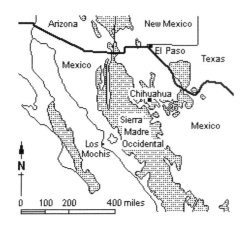

Present-day distribution of Tertiary volcanic and volcaniclastic rocks in Mexico and the southwest United States

mid-Atlantic ridge over the last 180 million years. In effect, the continent has been moving west over the earth's mantle, and this may have caused the disruptions on the surface above.

Igneous Rocks

A period of intense igneous activity began in the southwest United States and in Mexico at about 47 Ma, not long after the end of the main Laramide activity. It lasted for 25 million years and produced vast amounts of igneous rocks over the area shown on the map above. The most popular explanation for this event is that it resulted from the Farallon plate being subducted under North America. Sediments and oceanic crust basalt when subducted carry water down with them into the subduction zone. By the time it reaches a depth of 60 miles, about 50 miles inland from the subduction zone, the water lowers the melting point of the mantle so that it melts, generating andesite, and to a lesser extent, basalt, which finds their way to the surface and erupt to form an arc of volcanoes parallel to the subduction zone. Later, the lower part of the continental crust melts, creating large volumes of granitic magma. Some of this rises to the surface as lava; most remains underground as large granite intrusions called batholiths.

The Sierra Madre Occidental igneous rocks follow this pattern to some extent. They begin about 50 miles inland from the subduction zone, which roughly followed the California coast, and large granite intrusions occur near the coast. However, volcanic rocks continue east for another 250 miles to Chihuahua. Scattered centers beyond Chihuahua are as much as 500 miles inland from the plate boundary, the furthest east being the Davis Mountains. In the early days of plate tectonics, this wide zone of volcanic rocks was attributed to the angle of subduction of the Farallon plate, which is lower than normal, but several other hypotheses have been advanced more recently. One that has gained support argues that the North American crust, thickened during the Laramide Orogeny, generated so much heat from stretching in the Basin and Range episode that the crust was partially melted, thereby resulting in igneous activity.

Big Bend volcanic activity began with the eruption of basalt near the Rio Grande. Basalt melts at about 1,250 degrees Centigrade, and is about as runny as molasses when liquid. It can flow for long distances in thin sheets; the television shots you see of lava flows in Hawaii are of basalt. After the initial basalt eruptions, most Big Bend and Mexican magmas were granitic in composition, creating either rhyolite, the fine-grained equivalent of granite, or trachyte lava, which is slightly less silica-rich. Granitic lavas when liquid are usually quite viscous, rather like oatmeal; they melt at about 750 degrees Centigrade. If they contain water or come into contact with water, the water becomes superheated and the lavas explode on release of pressure, creating clouds of dust and ash. A recent U.S. example was the 1980 eruption of Mount St. Helens in Washington State in which the whole side of the mountain blew off and scattered ash up to 300 miles downwind. If granitic lavas do not contain water, they ooze out and create volcanic domes. Volcanic domes are quite common in the Big Bend, the most beautiful example being Casa Grande in the Chisos Basin, in which the upper 1,300 feet is a volcanic dome.

Volcanic ash began drifting into Big Bend National Park about 47 Ma, probably from water-bearing granitic magma erupting in Mexico; no volcanoes were active in Texas then. The ash is found as far north as the Davis Mountains but is not dated there. We only know that it predates the earliest lavas found, the Crossen and Star Mountain lavas that first appeared in 37 Ma. Local lavas and ash began to be produced widely at about that time. The map on the following page shows their extent and age and the known calderas resulting from their eruption. (Lavas south of Highway 90 and west of Highway 17 are not shown on the map). A caldera is a depression that forms after prolonged volcanic eruption empties a magma chamber and its roof collapses. During and just after the volcanic period, many igneous intrusions were created, some in the volcanic blanket, some in the underlying sedimentary rocks. Chemically, the intrusive rocks are very similar to the volcanic lavas, and they were undoubtedly derived from the same underlying pools of magma. They simply did not rise to the surface but were uncovered by erosion later.

Plants and fossils show that the climate during this period was mild with plentiful rain. The supply of ash was intermittent, and streams and lakes often formed on the surface of the ash beds. Beds of freshwater limestone are common, usually several feet thick.

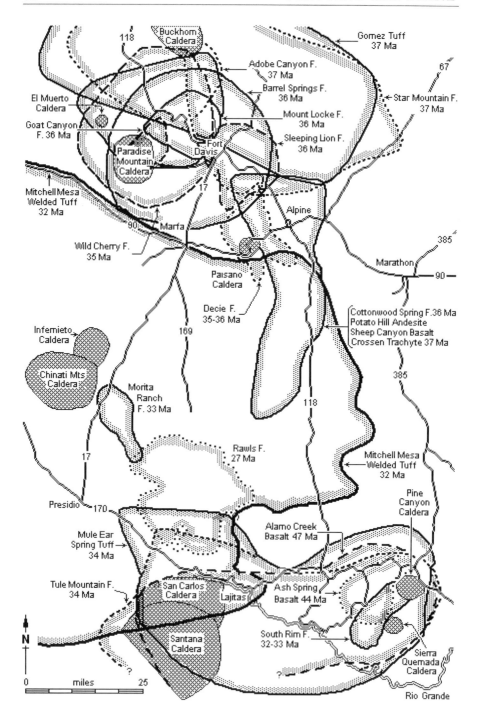

Local Sources of Lavas and Ash Falls in the Big Bend

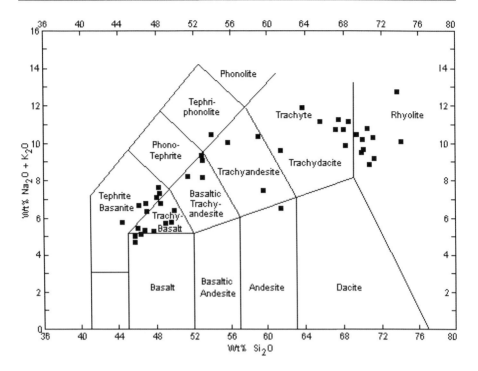

Chemical composition of lavas around Alpine

Volcanic ash is made up of particles of glass or pumice, glass with voids in it. It is chemically unstable and changes over time into clay creating a soft rock called tuff, a mixture of clay and glass. The rain eroded the tuff and redeposited it as sandstone or mudstone; sedimentary rocks made up of volcanic rock fragments are called volcaniclastics. Many early ash beds have been converted into volcaniclastics, which also occur between later lava beds and around the fringes of lava flows. Igneous activity was concluded by widespread basaltic eruptions at about 22 Ma. By then, a blanket of volcanic and volcaniclastic rocks up to 6,000 feet thick covered most of the Big Bend.

One of the main ways of classifying igneous rocks is by the TAS method, where the silica content of a rock is plotted against its combined sodium and potassium oxide or alkali content. The TAS diagram above is for lavas in the Alpine area but is representative of the Big Bend as a whole. The lavas fall into two groups, one around trachybasalt, a rock somewhat more alkali than normal basalt, and the other in the trachyte to rhyolite range, with a few scattered results in between.

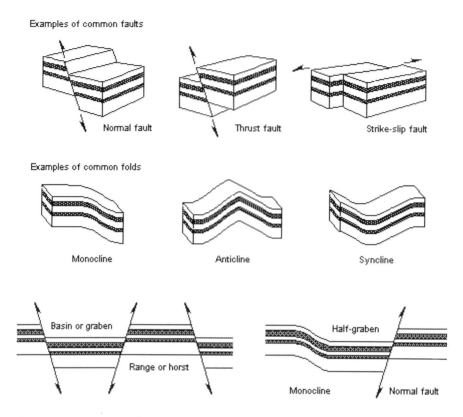

Examples of common faults

Normal fault   Thrust fault   Strike-slip fault

Examples of common folds

Monocline   Anticline   Syncline

Basin or graben   Half-graben

Range or horst

Monocline   Normal fault

Common structures in the Big Bend

Folding and Faulting

Big Bend strata have been much faulted and folded and various kinds of faults and folds are referred to repeatedly in the following chapters. The most common kinds are shown in the diagram above. Compression of the earth's crust, as in the Laramide Orogeny, creates thrust faults in which the crust is shortened. Stretching of the crust, as in the Basin and Range episode, creates normal faults. Strata move horizontally in strike-slip faults, either to the right in a right-lateral fault, or to the left in a left-lateral fault, as in the diagram above. Steep slopes or escarpments, called fault scarps by geologists, often form along the exposed surfaces of faults, especially normal faults, and are then eroded. They are among the most common landforms in the Big Bend.

Like thrust faults, most folding results from compression of the earth's crust. The two main kinds of folds are anticlines, in which strata are folded up into an arch-like structure, and synclines, where strata are folded down

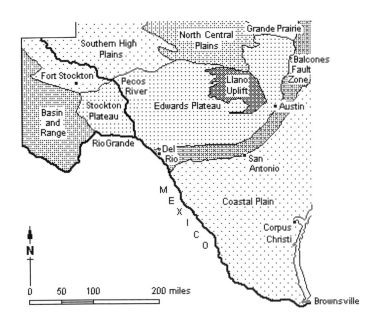

Physiographic regions of South Texas

into a trough. They often occur side by side. Monoclines, also known as drape folds, are a feature of extension, occurring where strata drape over an underlying fault. They are quite common in Big Bend limestone strata, which are flexible enough to be deformed in this way. Extension has created basins or grabens and ranges or horsts in the Southwest U.S. If large enough, grabens become rift valleys. Basins and ranges are usually bounded by normal faults but sometimes a monocline can substitute for one of the faults, as in the lower right of the diagram on the opposite page. If the monocline is of low amplitude or absent, the result is called a half graben.

Physiographic Provinces

The Bureau of Economic Geology divides South Texas into the physiographic provinces shown on the map above. Physiography, from the Greek words 'nature' and 'to write', is the description and nature of landforms and a physiographic province is one whose pattern of landforms is different from its neighboring provinces. The Big Bend is in the Stockton Plateau and Basin and Range provinces. Both merge into the Southern High Plains near Fort Stockton.

The Stockton Plateau is the continuation of the Edwards Plateau west of the Pecos River. It dates from about 10 million years ago, when strata west of the Balcones Fault began to be uplifted along the fault. This fault, really a broad fault zone, runs southwest across Texas from just west of Dallas through Austin and San Antonio to the Rio Grande valley near Del Rio. The zone closely follows the line of the Marathon-Ouachita mountain range along the ancient North American continental margin (see the Ouachita Front map on page 41). Strata west of the fault zone were uplifted as much as 2,000 feet and remained mostly flat lying.

Cretaceous sedimentary rocks east of Highways 385 and 2627 are in the Stockton Plateau. The plateau has been heavily eroded and in many areas only scattered mesas and buttes remain, interspersed with canyons and lowlands such as those along the road between Fort Stockton and Sierra Madera. They mostly rise 250-300 feet above the lowlands except around the Marathon Basin where escarpments are from 700 to 1,500 feet high. The strata thin and dip north from the Marathon Basin as the landscape merges into the Southern High Plains. They dip under Davis Mountains volcanic rocks on the west of the Basin.

On the east and south of the Marathon Basin, canyon bottoms and alluvial flats fall away at about 40 feet to the mile. Stretches of water-carried rock rubble, sand and gravel litter the base of hills, typical of desert landscapes, where rapid-flowing bursts of water can carry quite large rocks along with them. The landscape is starker than it is further east, the corners sharper, and the canyons steeper because of the lower rainfall; rainfall rounds and softens landscapes. Streams have mostly reached balance between erosion and deposition, except along the Pecos River and especially the Rio Grande, where Cretaceous strata are eroding back from the river in deep canyons.

The Marathon Basin has its own unique physiography within the Stockton Plateau. In it, anticlines of chert and other erosion-resistant sedimentary rocks have created ridges running north-northeast at right angles to the direction of thrusting during the Ouachita Orogeny. Except on the west, limestone escarpments rim the basin dipping away from it at between 5 and 15 degrees. The narrow monoclinal ridge of the Del Norte and Santiago Mountains are on the western perimeter. The Glass Mountains and the Marathon Basin are described in Chapter II.

The country west of Highway 385 and FM 2627 is in the Basin and Range physiographic province. In this province, north-south trending mountain ranges typically alternate with flat-bottomed valley floors, as in New Mexico and Arizona. The Big Bend is at its very eastern boundary. Although large vertical movements have taken place at some places in the Big Bend, the Franklin Mountains horst at El Paso, for example, is more than 25,000 feet above the floor of the original basin, the basins and ranges in the Big Bend are less dramatic. However, they add variety to the landscape, mostly as flat-bottomed plains between fault scarps.

The Influence of Geology on Landscapes

The Basin and Range province in the Big Bend has many other landscape features. Landscapes are mostly controlled by the underlying geology and Big Bend geology is complex and varied. The geological map on page 26 shows how strata are distributed at the surface today. Volcanic rocks underlie the biggest part of the area, along its western edge from Fort Davis to Lajitas, and in the Chisos Mountains between Panther Junction and Castolon. Cretaceous limestones lie beneath most of the east and south. Paleozoic rocks of the Marathon Basin and the Glass Mountains underlie a large area in the north center of the map. Igneous intrusions are widespread and mostly quite small. Conglomerates, sandstones and siltstones fill grabens on either side of the Dead Horse Mountains and around Castolon. Small areas of soft Tertiary-age non-marine sedimentary rocks occur near Panther Junction.

Lavas and igneous intrusions create the most striking landscapes. Lavas of rhyolite or trachyte, found near eruptive centers, form caps on mesas and buttes that weather to a dark gray or dark red brown color. Joints form as the magma contracts when it cools, especially in the smaller bodies that cool quickly. Lava beds are usually jointed vertically and break up as they erode. As a consequence, lava mesas and buttes tend to have many more boulders lying on them than limestone ones, giving them a characteristic dark, rough, ragged look. Buttes degenerate into rough pyramids as they erode; many can be seen around the Big Bend, at the entrance to Sunny Glen canyon near Alpine, for example. Rhyolite and trachyte lavas thin and die out away from volcanic centers leaving only tuff and volcaniclastic sedimentary rocks; these tend to be soft and easily eroded. They form low, rolling hills, and seldom crop out except in road cuts and streambeds, and along escarpments where they sometimes show up as horizontal gray streaks.

Enormous numbers of igneous intrusions occur in a belt running northwest from Rio Grande Village to Fort Davis and beyond. Most were created at quite shallow depths, less than 3,000 feet, and are fine grained; shallow intrusions cool faster than deep ones, and crystals have less time to grow. Many Big Bend intrusions are jointed, too. When jointed, they often form pinnacles, such as those on Pulliam Peak or Mitre Peak. A beautiful example is Willow Mountain near Study Butte, which is so intensely jointed that the mountain looks from a distance as if it were striated, with individual joints running several hundred feet down its sides.

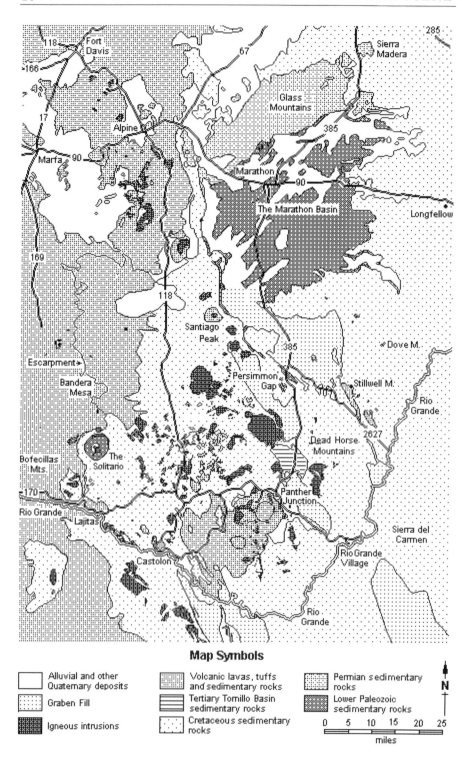

Map Symbols

- Alluvial and other Quatemary deposits
- Graben Fill
- Igneous intrusions
- Volcanic lavas, tuffs and sedimentary rocks
- Tertiary Tornillo Basin sedimentary rocks
- Cretaceous sedimentary rocks
- Permian sedimentary rocks
- Lower Paleozoic sedimentary rocks

N

0   5   10   15   20   25
miles

Geology of the Big Bend

Geologists classify intrusions by shape and, to some extent, size. A tabular or sheet-like body is called a *sill* if it has been injected parallel to the bedding in its host rock. The shape of an uncovered intrusion depends partly on the shape of the original intrusion, so sills, being parallel to the beds into which they were injected, are horizontal or near horizontal, and cap mesas when uncovered. Elephant Mountain and Nine Point Mesa south of Alpine are two of the most prominent examples in the Big Bend.

If a tabular-shaped intrusion crosscuts the bedding of its host rock, it is called a *dike*. Dikes are usually nearly vertical and create ridges with rocks outcropping at their crests with cockscomb or iguana lizard profiles. Many examples can be seen near Paisano Peak on the Alpine-Marfa road, Lizard Mountain for example, and at the Fins of Fire exhibit on Ross Maxwell Drive in the National Park.

A *laccolith* is a sill that domes the beds above it, forming a mushroom-shaped body. Laccoliths are common in the area and tend to produce mushroom-shaped mountains. Examples include the Rosillos Mountains north of the Park, Maverick Mountain east of Study Butte, and the Barillos Dome north of Alpine.

A *stock* is an igneous mass with less than 40 square miles of surface exposure and no known floor. Stocks stand up as sizeable mountains when uncovered. The Cienega Mountain - Haley Mountain - McIntyre Peak intrusion south of Alpine and the Chisos Mountains pluton are two of the most prominent.

A *plug* is a vertical, pipe-like body, sometimes a filled volcanic vent, also called a volcanic *neck*, or a solidified intrusion feeder. Plugs or volcanic necks are cylindrical bodies that when eroded narrow toward their peaks. Examples are Mitre Peak near Alpine and Hen Egg Mountain north of Study Butte.

West of the Del Norte-Santiago-Dead Horse Mountains, Cretaceous strata are less heavily eroded than in the Stockton Plateau, perhaps because volcanic strata covered much of the area until recently. From the Solitario to Alpine, Cretaceous flaggy limestones predominate, forming low rolling hills. Uplands, such as the Mesa de Anguila or the Terlingua Uplift, have been stripped of their Upper Cretaceous strata, usually down to the Santa Elena Limestone. Upper Cretaceous non-marine claystones and sandstones remain in the basins and form flats or badlands. Small areas of Tertiary non-marine sedimentary rocks occur around the Chisos Mountains, mostly in Tornillo Flat. They also form badlands, often multicolored and quite picturesque.

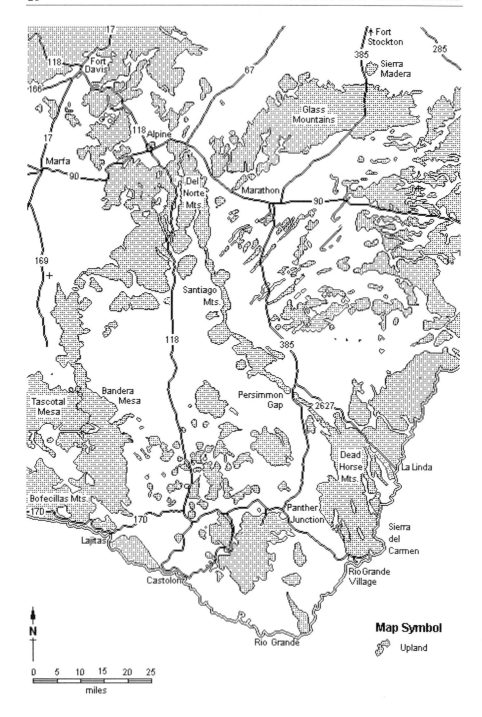

Uplands in the Big Bend

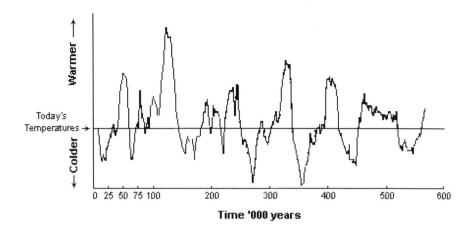

Climate fluctuations in the Southwest over the last 600,000 years

As shown on the map opposite, about 30 per cent of the map area is upland, the remainder lowland, typical for a moderately mature semi-arid landscape. Uplands run mainly northwest southeast, except in the Glass Mountains and around Marathon where they run northeast southwest. Lowlands descend to the Rio Grande at about 40 feet per mile and to the Pecos River at about 20 feet per mile. The greatest vertical relief in the area is along the Rio Grande where at Rio Grande Village, for example, the Chisos Mountains tower almost 6,000 feet above the visitor center. Elsewhere in the area, there are a few mountains with relief above 2,000 feet but most rise 500 to 2,000 feet above their bases.

The Influence of Climate on Landscapes

Climate is another important factor in creating landscapes. Climates in the Southwest over the past 600,000 years have been well established through studying fluctuations in the amounts of an oxygen isotope, O^{18}, present in calcite deposited in stalactites and stalagmites in underground caverns. The isotope content is higher in warm periods than in cold. The graph above developed using this method shows that temperatures have varied considerably over the period, with cold cycles occurring at least once every hundred thousand years and lasting for tens of thousands of years. The last really cold period, the last Ice Age, ended about 10,000 years ago. Cold periods are wetter than warm periods. Compared to today's climate, temperatures over the past 600,000 years were more often higher than lower, certainly for the last 150,000 years, and desert conditions were more common than temperate, wetter conditions.

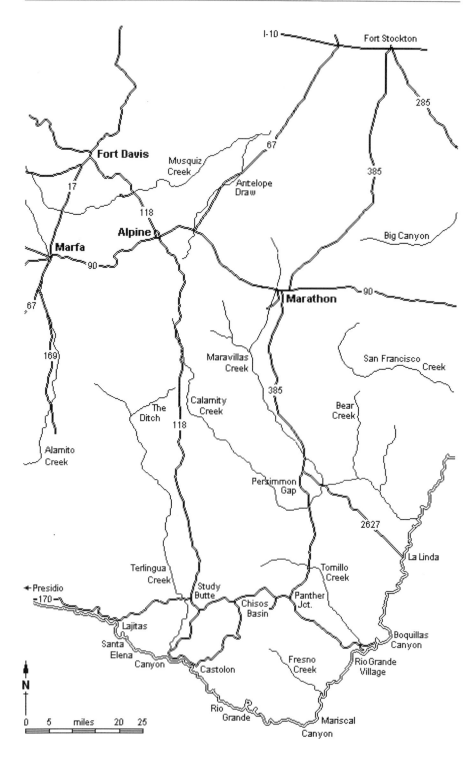

Drainage in the Big Bend

In general, basins fill with sediments in arid periods. Rocks have little vegetation on them and rainfall and temperature changes break them up faster than the limited water runoff can carry them away, so the basins fill up. In wet periods, the opposite is true; vegetation limits erosion and ample water carries away all the sediments, so basins empty. In the Big Bend, huge alluvial and conglomerate fans such as the Fingers Formation are evidence of dry periods.

Study of these deposits shows that there have been four major dry periods in the last 25 million years: 24 to 22 Ma, 19 to 18 Ma, at 10 Ma and 1.5 Ma to the present. Wet periods leave less direct evidence. Evidence from the Gulf of Mexico, however, shows that rivers began to remove material from the hinterland as soon as volcanic activity began and many thousand feet of lava, ash and sedimentary rocks have been removed from the southern National Park since the end of the volcanic era.

Today, the Big Bend is in the northern Chihuahua Desert and the landscape is predominantly a desert one. Rainfall is sparse; the average annual rainfall is between 6 and 7 inches on the Rio Grande at Castolon, at about 2,000 feet elevation. It increases at higher elevations, 15 inches at Panther Junction (3,750 feet), 16 inches in the Chisos Basin (5,400 feet) and at Alpine (4,500 feet). Temperatures also vary with altitude. In Alpine or Marathon, the climate is temperate, seldom below freezing in the winter, seldom above 100 degrees in the summer. Down on the river, temperatures are 10 to 20 degrees hotter, pleasant in the winter but trying in the summer.

Three quarters of the annual rainfall falls from April to September, mostly from July to September when moist air circulating anticlockwise around a low-pressure area near Bermuda creates numerous thunderstorms. Hurricanes and tropical storms occasionally bring heavy rain to the region in the late summer from either the Gulf of California or the Gulf of Mexico. Rain usually falls in thundershowers, sometimes as much as several inches at a time, so the area gets frequent light scattered showers and several heavy downpours over the summer, with the rest of the year being very dry. Snow usually falls several times during an average winter, but does not stay long.

In the desert, moderate rain showers cause streams to run for a time, run-off dissipating into the alluvium a few miles downstream. However, heavy thunderstorms occasionally create dangerous floods. The major watercourses drain very large areas; Terlingua Creek, flowing just west of Study Butte, drains 1,315 square miles, Maravillas Creek, 1,950 square miles. Even Tornillo Creek in the National Park, only 30 miles long, drains 350 square miles. An inch of rainfall produces 22,700 gallons per acre so these large areas can collect enormous amounts of rainwater. For example, an inch of rain in the Tornillo Creek basin generates 5 billion gallons. As a result, a creek can quickly turn into a raging torrent for a few hours after a heavy rainstorm, and move a great deal of eroded material downstream.

An arid or semi-arid climate creates a characteristic landscape of flat or nearly flat plains between uplands flanked by steep escarpments. The proportion of upland to lowland depends on the age of the landscape and the resistance of the underlying rocks to erosion. Plateaus or mesas develop where flat-lying erosion-resistant rocks, such as a limestone beds or lava flows, cap uplands. Vertical or near-vertical cliffs develop below the caprock and steep slopes of rubble run down to the plain below. Heavy rains create ravines or gullies in the rubble and if soft sedimentary rocks are exposed, they wash away progressively, undercutting the caprock. Eventually, a section of caprock collapses, leaving a scar; this is one of the ways in which an escarpment retreats. At its base, a pediment forms, a gently sloping surface usually covered by a layer of pebbles and finer rock particles called alluvium. In places, where a stream runs off an upland, an alluvial fan may develop, a fan-shaped blanket of rocks of all sizes.

Drainage Patterns

Drainage in the Big Bend is dominated by the Rio Grande. The first major river to come into existence, however, was the Pecos River, which rises in the Sangre de Christo Mountains in New Mexico, and was completed across Texas by about 10 million years ago. Early drainage off the volcanic highlands in the Big Bend appears to have flowed east into the Pecos River or a predecessor. Many of today's streams, San Francisco Creek, Maravillas Creek and Nine Point Draw, for example, flow east until captured by south flowing streams. Next to develop was the Rio Conchos, which drains the Sierra Madre Occidental and now joins the Rio Grande at Presidio. It followed today's Rio Grande course through a saddle in the Dead Horse Mountains at Boquillas to the Pecos River near Del Rio, 180 miles downstream. Lastly, the Rio Grande developed from basin to basin down the Rio Grande Rift from southern Colorado through New Mexico and met the Rio Conchos in a large basin at Presidio. Sedimentary evidence in New Mexico shows that this process was completed about 2.25 million years ago.

Today, the Rio Grande flows in a channel from Del Rio upstream to La Linda. The channel is 300 feet deep at the junction with the Pecos River. It deepens steadily to nearly 1,000 feet at La Linda. From La Linda upstream, it runs through Basin and Range grabens linked by short canyons up to 1,600 feet high. Local drainage flows into the Pecos River or the Rio Grande. The divide between the two drainage basins is 10 miles south and 12 miles east of Alpine. The most important watercourse going north to the Pecos River is Musquiz Creek, which rises in the Puertacitas Mountains and flows through the Alpine basin where it is joined by Alpine Creek. It ends at the Pecos River, 90 miles north and 3,000 feet below its source.

The main Rio Grande tributaries in the Big Bend are Terlingua and Maravillas Creeks, both over 60 miles long. Maravillas Creek originates in the Glass and Del Norte Mountains. Terlingua Creek rises in Cartwright Mesa west of Green Valley. Big Canyon is the major watercourse north of Marathon. It rises in the Dimple Hills and flows east before turning south to join the Rio Grande 80 miles southeast of its source. It is another example of a stream that appears to have been captured by the Rio Grande after initially draining into the Pecos.

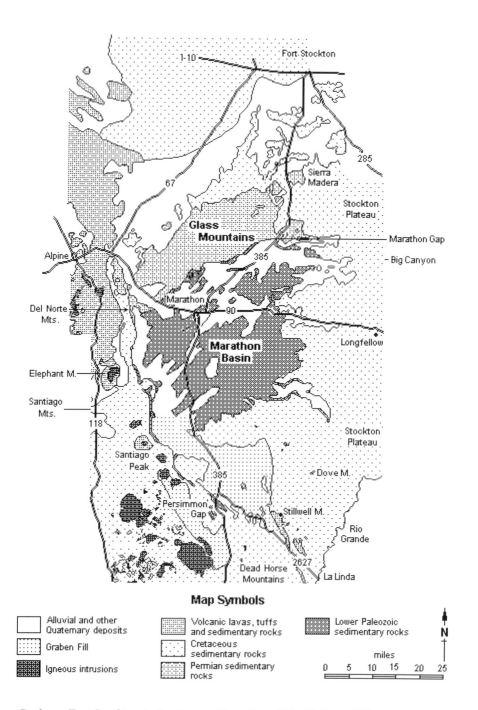

Map Symbols

Alluvial and other Quaternary deposits	
Graben Fill	
Igneous intrusions	
Volcanic lavas, tuffs and sedimentary rocks	
Cretaceous sedimentary rocks	
Permian sedimentary rocks	
Lower Paleozoic sedimentary rocks	

N

miles

0   5   10   15   20   25

Geology: Fort Stockton to Persimmon Gap along U.S. Highway 385

II The Glass Mountains & the Marathon Basin

The Glass Mountains and the Marathon Basin introduce the Big Bend to most visitors on their way to Big Bend National Park. Both are structures with complex histories that are still not fully unraveled after a century of study. An area overall of tremendous diversity, the landscapes include the Stockton Plateau, the Marathon Basin, the Glass Mountains, the Basin and Range Black Gap Graben, and the Laramide Del Norte and Santiago Mountains. The chapter begins by recounting the geological history of the area and explaining the structures through cross sections and maps.

The Marathon Dome and the Del Norte Mountains

The story begins near the end of the Cretaceous period, 70 million years ago, 5 million years after the ocean had withdrawn across the Big Bend. Texas had been long under a shallow sea, the Western Interior Seaway. Thick limestone beds had built up on the ocean floor from the Hill Country west across the Big Bend.

During the Laramide Orogeny, 70 to 50 Ma, east-west compression created the Del Norte and Santiago Mountains and on their east, a low swell around the town of Marathon that geologists call the Marathon Dome. Although the word dome conjures up visions of a mountain rising up dramatically from the plain, the Marathon Dome was in reality a quite low structure, rising only about 4,500 feet above its surroundings. It might be better to call it a low swell rather than a dome. The upper diagram on the next page, drawn to scale, shows how the Dome might have looked in cross section when it was created.

The Del Norte-Santiago Mountains are part of a mountain range that runs 90 miles south-southeast from Highway 90 to the Rio Grande and continues for another 80 miles in Mexico. The mountains are the eroded

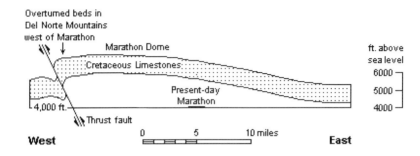

Section through the Marathon Dome and Del Norte Mountains when they were first created. The overturned monocline on the west was thrust faulted along much of its length.

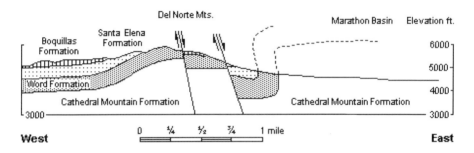

Section through the Del Norte Mountains today south of Dugout Mountain

remains of an overturned monocline that developed at the western edge of the Marathon Dome when the dome was created. The monocline was thrust-faulted along much of its length with strata on the east riding up over strata on the west. The most northerly thrust fault, exposed from Dugout Mountain to Santiago Peak, has a maximum uplift of about 2,000 feet near Black Peak.

The mountains are as much as 5 miles wide for the first 20 miles south of Highway 90 but then narrow to a ridge not much more than a mile wide for the next 40 miles. The name changes to the Santiago Mountains at Del Norte Gap, 26 miles south of Highway 90, but the geological structure remains the same. The monocline dies away north of Highway 90 into a broad anticline that disappears under volcanic strata.

The Earth's crust began to be extended or stretched across the Big Bend during the Basin and Range period and strata on the Marathon side of the Del Norte and Santiago Mountains were downfaulted beginning at about 28 Ma. In places, the thrust faults created 20 to 40 million years earlier were reused. In other places, normal faults developed along the mountains to the east of the thrust faults.

The upper part of the monocline has been eroded away, leaving a ridge with sharply folded beds standing above the surrounding flats on either side. The lower sketch opposite is a section through the Del Norte Mountains today near the southern end of Dugout Mountain. Two normal faults drop beds to the east, the range not being thrust faulted in this cross section.

The Marathon Basin

The central cover of the Marathon Dome has also been removed by erosion, revealing the Marathon Basin, a low area around the town of Marathon, 30 miles east to west by 40 miles north to south. In it, heavily crumpled and faulted Paleozoic rocks crop out in a series of low brown ridges running northeast southwest across beautiful grassland flats. The basin is surrounded by escarpments on the east and south, the Del Norte Mountains to the west and the Glass Mountains to the northwest. Strata dip away from the basin at between 5 and 15 degrees, creating cuestas in the Glass Mountains and in the Maravillas Escarpment to the south.

The Marathon Basin is a window into the ancient past. It reveals a complex story, one that was not solved by geologists until the theory of plate tectonics was developed in the period 1965-1975. Then it became evident that the Marathon Basin is at the western end of a fold belt that was created when two continental groups, Laurasia and Gondwana, collided at the beginning of the Permian period, 280 million years ago, to form a single land mass called Pangea. The fold belt extended from the Big Bend to the Black Sea at the eastern edge of Europe, and mountains developed along it in events called orogenies, or mountain-building episodes. Mountains formed across southern Europe and North Africa in the Variscan Orogeny; the southern Appalachians formed along the eastern seaboard of the United States in the late Alleghanian Orogeny; and the Ouachita Mountains formed in Oklahoma and Arkansas in the Ouachita Orogeny.

Marathon Basin strata are very similar to those in the Ouachita Mountains and geologists believe that they are the roots of mountains formed in the Ouachita Orogeny and that the Ouachita Mountains originally extended from the Texas-Arkansas border through the Marathon Basin at least as far as Lajitas on the Rio Grande. During the orogeny, ocean floor sedimentary rocks were thrust and crumpled on to the North American continent over younger sedimentary rocks. The oldest rocks telescoped onto the continent, the Dagger Flat Sandstone through the Caballos Novaculite (see strata table on pages 38-39), were laid down slowly in the deep ocean off the south coast of North America, distant from sources of sediment.

Period Name	Age m.y.	Formation	Description
Lower Cretaceous	144-98	Washita Group	Upper part fine grained, hard, massive, poorly bedded to nodular Buda Limestone, light gray to orange, weathers dark gray to brown; 100 feet thick; lower part Del Rio Formation marl; 130 ft. thick.
		Fredericksburg Group	Limestone, dolomite, chert and minor marl of the Santa Elena and Del Carmen Formations; 135-200 ft. thick.
		Trinity Group	Sandstone, fine to coarse grained, of the Maxon and Glen Rose Formations, becoming conglomeratic northwards; up to 100 ft. thick.
		Bissett Conglomerate	Limestone, dolomite and quartz pebbles with interbedded limestone and brownish yellow to red shale; up to 700 ft. thick.
Permian	286-245	Tessey Limestone	Massive, in part dolomitic, light yellowish brown to gray; 1,000 ft. thick.
		Capitan Limestone	To the northeast, thin-bedded becoming massive southwestward, overlies massive dolomitic limestone reef; to the southwest, siliceous shale and thin-bedded limestone near middle, yellowish brown, white, light gray; up to 1,800 ft. thick.
		Word	Siliceous shale and clay shale with thin units of limestone containing fossils, sandstone and conglomerate; up to 1,500 ft. thick.
		Cathedral Mountain	Siliceous shale, chert, interbedded limestone and conglomerate, yellow, orange; weathers pink and red; 1,600 ft. thick.
		Skinner Ranch and Hess Limestone	Limestone, thick beds of limestone-pebble conglomerate in lower part, minor amounts of interbedded shale, 225-1,600 ft. thick. Merges eastward with thin-bedded Hess Limestone, much of which is dolomitized; 1,600-2,300 ft. thick.
		Lenox Hills Formation	Conglomerate, shale, limestone and dolomite; 30-675 ft. thick, changing rapidly from place to place.
		Neal Ranch Formation	Shale, limestone and some conglomerate towards base; 300 ft thick.
Pennsylvanian	320-286	Gaptank	Thick layers of limestone interbedded with sandstone and shale, 800 ft. thick, followed by 900 ft. of inter-bedded sandstone, shale and coarse conglomerate and a basal 100-ft. thick limestone; formation 1,800 ft. thick at maximum.
		Haymond	Sandstone and carbonaceous shale in regular rhythmic alternations, with an occasional thicker sandstone bed, and near the base, some thicker layers of shale; in upper part, thick beds of massive coarse-grained feldspar-rich sandstone and several boulder-bearing mudstone intervals as much as 150 ft. thick; formation >3,000 ft. thick.
		Dimple	Mostly granular, somewhat sandy, cherty, gray, moderately thick limestone beds; other beds very fine grained, very bituminous; to the east much shale in upper and lower parts; 300-1,000 ft. thick.

Period Name	Age m.y.	Formation	Description
Upper Mississippian- Lower Pennsylvanian	345- 310	Tesnus	In southeastern area, upper 5,000 ft., thin- to thick-bedded sandstone and shale, with massive white quartz intervals in upper part; lower 2,000 ft., shale. In northwestern area, nearly all black shale, with few sandstone beds, about 300 ft. thick; formation 300-7,000 ft. thick.
Silurian- Devonian	438- 360	Caballos Novaculite	Chert and novaculite; novaculite, massive, white; chert, varicolored, bedded; 200-600 ft. thick.
Ordovician	495- 438	Maravillas Chert	Bedded black chert and thin-bedded dark gray to black limestone; 100-400 ft. thick.
		Woods Hollow Shale	Greenish clay shale with interbedded gray to yellowish sandy limestone and limy sandstone; 300-400 ft. thick.
		Fort Pena	Thick-bedded limestone alternating with bedded bluish and purplish chert; near base one or more beds of coarse conglomerate; 125-200 ft. thick.
		Alsate Shale	In northern area, hard green shale, thin limestone beds common in south; conglomerate locally at base; 24-145 ft. thick.
		Marathon Shale	Flaggy dark-gray to gray-black limestone, weathers ashen gray with shale intervals and partings; 350-1,000 ft. thick.
Upper Cambrian- Ordovician	515- 495	Dagger Flat Sandstone	Medium-grained, massive l sandstone interbedded with shale; brownish yellow, weathers light brown; about 300 ft. thick, base not exposed.

Strata in the Glass Mountains and the Marathon Basin

In the first 170 million years, 300 feet of sandstone were deposited, followed by 2,700 feet of thin beds of silica-rich fine-grained cherts, novaculites and shales. Chert and novaculite are siliceous rocks whose silica was largely derived from sponge and radiolarian skeletons; a radiolarian is a single-celled organism with a silica skeleton. The map on page 40 shows the two continental blocks during the Pennsylvanian period at about 325 Ma, shortly before they collided.

By the middle of the Mississippian period, 340 Ma, as Laurasia approached Gondwana, the water deepened and mountains developed in both continents. The pace of sedimentation quickened; 14,000 feet of sandstone, shale and limestone of the Gaptank, Tesnus, Dimple and Haymond Formations were created in the next 60 million years. Many of these sedimentary rocks are turbidites and include blocks of limestone and other boulders torn off existing rock formations.

In the final episode of the Orogeny, which took place after the Permian Neal Ranch Formation was deposited, ocean sedimentary rocks were thrust

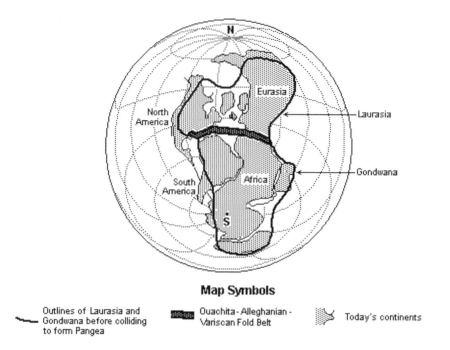

Map Symbols

Outlines of Laurasia and Gondwana before colliding to form Pangea	Ouachita-Alleghanian-Variscan Fold Belt	Today's continents

Laurasia and Gondwana came together in the late Paleozoic to form Pangea. The collision between the two gave rise to a fold belt with the Ouachita-Marathon Mountains at its western extremity and the southern Appalachians next to them.

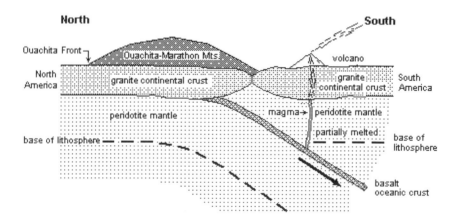

Ouachita Orogeny: Laurasia collided with Gondwana thrusting sea-floor sedimentary rocks on to the North American continent

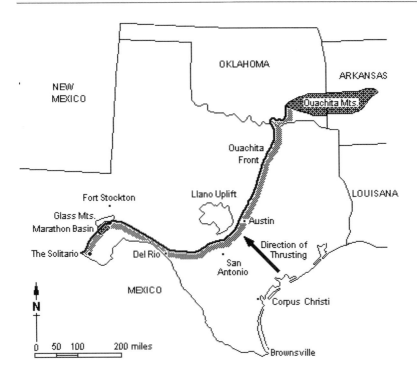

The Ouachita Front today crops out in the Ouachita Mountains in Oklahoma, in the Marathon Basin and at the Solitario

and crumpled over younger strata. In places, the strata were shortened by as much as 80 per cent, and some beds crop out repeatedly, as shown in the cross section on page 43. Geologists call a rock mass that has been moved from its place of origin an allochthon. The join or suture between Laurasia and Gondwana has not been found in Texas, so the Marathon Basin sedimentary rocks must have been pushed northwest at least 125 miles. The sea withdrew for 10 million years after the orogeny ended, and the mountains and the allochthon were eroded down to a plain.

Today, the allochthon is wedge-shaped, thickening to the southeast. Its lower surface is the Dugout Creek overthrust, a thrust fault dipping about 10 degrees to the southeast. The northern limit of the allochthon, the Ouachita Front, crops out west of Marathon in Dugout Creek and elsewhere is inferred from intersections in oil exploration wells. It crosses under the Glass Mountains, dips south to Del Rio, and heads northeast to Oklahoma and Arkansas as shown on the map above. Its position in the Marathon Basin and the Glass Mountains is shown in more detail in the map on page 48.

Physiography of the Glass Mountains and the Marathon Basin

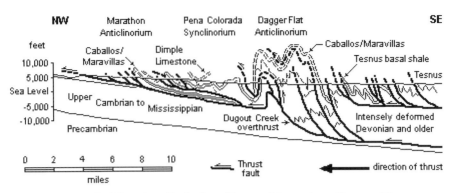

Section across the Marathon Basin from Dugout Mountain to Dagger Flat

In the Marathon Basin today, the older sedimentary rocks are mostly found south of Highway 90 where the corrugated roots of the Ouachita-Marathon Mountains stand up as sharp ridges called hogbacks. The older rocks contain beds of chert in the Maravillas Chert and Caballos Novaculite Formations (novaculite is a variety of chert used for whetstones in Arkansas), flanked by soft shale of the Tesnus and Woods Hollow Shale Formations. The shale has eroded away leaving chert beds standing up as sharp ridges called hogbacks. Here and there, where a resistant bed runs parallel to the side of a ridge, overlying material has fallen off exposing the white chert bed in a series of scalloped outcrops called flatirons from their shapes.

Two fan-like series of anticlines and synclines called anticlinoriums run southwest across the Marathon Basin perpendicular to the direction of thrusting. In an anticlinorium the overall effect is to lift up older rocks to the surface in the center of the structure. The Marathon Anticlinorium crosses the basin from a few miles north of Marathon to around Black Peak. The Dagger Flat Anticlinorium runs parallel to it from the Warwick Hills southwest. It has ridges on both flanks with Dagger Flat, an open flat area between them. Between the anticlinoriums lies the Pena Colorada Synclinorium, an anticlinorium upside down. Strata have been folded down in its center so that the younger rocks of the Haymond, Dimple and Tesnus Formations are at the surface. They rarely crop out, and a fine grassy plain stretches across the synclinorium. The above cross-section, from Dugout Mountain to Dagger Flat, shows all three major structures. The present-day physiography of the Marathon Basin is shown on the map opposite.

Tesnus, Dimple Limestone and Haymond strata of the Pennsylvanian and Mississippian periods make up most of the allochthon in the northwest

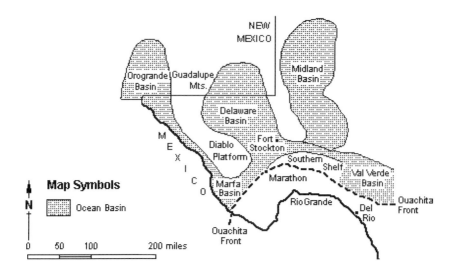

Permian ocean basins in Texas and New Mexico

basin. They are much thicker than the strata in the western basin and their folds are broader (compare the cross sections on pages 43 and 69). Only the Dimple Limestone is erosion-resistant. In several places, it has been brought to the surface by thrust faults to create prominent ridges. The Stillwell Mountain ridge, for example, has been caused by the Frog Creek Thrust fault. In the Dimple Hills, the crest of an anticlinorium has been down warped to create a basin of folded limestone.

Between the ridges, soft shales and sandstones underlie a fairly level plain sloping to the south at 30 feet per mile. The physiographic map on page 42 shows the ridges in the basin, the Glass Mountains and the surrounding Cretaceous escarpments. The conspicuous U-shaped outcrops south of Lemons Gap are the noses of anticlines dipping underground to the south. The horse's tail beyond Tres Hermanas is also an anticline, which has brought up Marathon Basin strata above their normal position.

The crests of the novaculite and chert ridges are noticeably even, standing 500-700 feet above the surrounding flats. The ridges diminish in height to the north and to the west, but the overall impression is of an earlier erosion surface about 4,400 or 4,500 feet above sea level that has been subsequently worn down to the present 4,000 feet. Horse Mountain (5,013 feet) is an exception, 1,375 feet above the plain and the highest point in the basin. The whale-backed ridge is an anticline in which a novaculite bed 600 feet thick is folded over the crest and has slowed down erosion. Bedrock is covered by gravel which is usually less than 20 feet thick although alluvial fans up to 100 feet thick have developed in places.

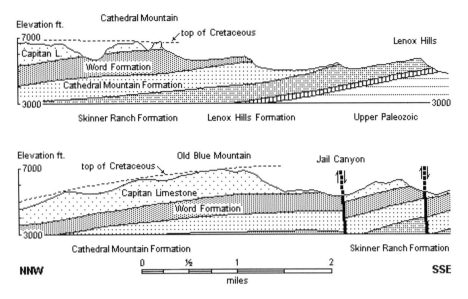

NNW-SSE Sections across Cathedral and Old Blue Mountains

The Glass Mountains

As North and South America came together in the Ouachita Orogeny shortly after the beginning of the Permian period, a series of ocean basins collectively known as the Permian Basin formed to the north and west of the Ouachita Thrust allochthon as shown in the map opposite. Marathon is on south coast of Hovey Channel, which connected the open ocean to the Delaware Basin. A thick series of Permian sedimentary rocks deposited along the coast of the Delaware Basin now crop out in the Glass Mountains, in Shafter, in the Guadalupe Mountains and in New Mexico. They were tilted 10 degrees or so to the northwest before being overlain by Cretaceous strata and were tilted a further 5 degrees when the Marathon Dome formed. The tilted Glass Mountain escarpments facing Marathon provide the best exposures of Permian sedimentary rocks in Texas and were intensely studied when oil and gas were first discovered in the Permian basin.

The Glass Mountain range is also the most complete section remaining of the Marathon Dome. It consists of a set of ridges, highest and most impressive at Highway 90, diminishing to the northeast across Highway 385 where they disappear into Stockton Plateau mesas. The cross sections above show how erosion-resistant beds in the strata have created three cuesta ridges. A cuesta is a hill or ridge with a steep slope or escarpment on one side and a gentle slope parallel to the strata on the other.

Capitan Limestone caps the highest and most spectacular of the cuestas. The limestone is a fossil reef, rather like the coral reefs of the Caribbean, but built by sponges, algae and by calcium carbonate cement precipitated from seawater. It is found all the way round the south coast of the Delaware Basin, and reaches its most spectacular development in the Guadalupe Mountains, 130 miles northwest of Marathon, where it takes its name from the highest mountain in Texas, the Capitan Peak of the Guadalupe Mountains. It crops out over most of the west-facing Glass Mountain slopes and caps the three highest peaks, Gilliland Peak (6,513 feet), Old Blue Mountain (6,286 feet), and Cathedral Mountain (6,220 feet).

Cathedral Mountain Formation, overlying Skinner Ranch and Lenox Hills Formations, creates the next highest set of cuestas. These include Dugout Mountain, the Lenox Hills and Leonard Mountain, all very well seen from Highway 90. The third set of cuestas, created by the Neal Ranch and Gaptank Formations at the base of the Permian, is a series of low hills along the front of the Glass Mountains from Marathon Gap on Highway 385 to the Wolfcamp Hills 10 miles southwest.

The Glass Mountains have been folded and faulted. The most prominent fold is an anticline running up Gilliland Canyon for 5 miles from Iron Mountain. The folding may have fractured the strata and helped the canyon develop. It then turns northwest along the crest of Old Blue Mountain parallel to a major fault. The anticline raises Permian strata 1,000 feet on the mountain ridge and explains why Old Blue is prominent so far west in the range (see page 234). The anticline continues northwest at least as far as the Orient rail line near Hovey. Forty normal faults have been identified crossing the mountains, the major ones being shown on the map on page 48. In places, they form grabens as in Hess Canyon midway up the range, where a block has been dropped down 500 feet to form a canyon 6 miles long. Elsewhere, the faulting created zones of broken rock that aided erosion, leading to canyons penetrating the range. The faulting is thought to be the same age as Basin and Range faulting.

The Glass Mountains decline into a less imposing, but very even-crested escarpment toward the east, and the cuesta-capping formations thin. Permian strata disappear under Cretaceous limestones east of Highway 385 at Marathon Gap.

Two road sections are described in this chapter. The first is along Highway 385 from Fort Stockton to Persimmon Gap. It crosses the Marathon Basin from north to south and the northeast corner of the Glass Mountains. The second is along U.S. Highway 90 from the Highway 67 junction east of Alpine to the abandoned railway station of Longfellow. It crosses the southwest tip of the Glass Mountains and the Marathon Basin from west to east.

U.S. 385 Fort Stockton – Persimmon Gap

101 Miles

The Fort Stockton-Persimmon Gap road begins where the Stockton Plateau from the east meets the Southern High Plains from the north, passes near the meteor impact site of Sierra Madera, and crosses the northeastern Glass Mountains. It then traverses the Marathon Basin through crumpled Paleozoic strata exposed in roadcuts and along ridges south of Marathon. It crosses the western tip of the Maravillas Escarpment on the basin's southern margin, and enters the Black Gap Graben, a grassy plain 12 miles across. The road climbs up through the Santiago Mountains to Persimmon Gap in its last mile. It provides wonderful vistas along the way; the vista on entering the Marathon Basin at Marathon Gap is particularly spectacular. Other fine vistas are the Del Norte and Santiago Mountains from south of Marathon, across the Black Gap graben to Dove Mountain from the junction of Highway 385 and FM 2627, and down the Black Gap graben to Pico Etereo in Mexico from the same point.

Mileages are measured from the intersection of Interstate 10 and Highway 385 in Fort Stockton to Highway 90 and from the intersection of Highway 90 and 385 in Marathon to Persimmon Gap. Strata in the Marathon Basin and the Glass Mountains are described in the table on pages 38-9.

Leaving Fort Stockton, the road runs south through alluvium-covered flats and scattered mesas for the first 20 miles, climbing at about 30 feet per mile towards Sierra Madera and the Glass Mountains on the horizon. Three-Mile Mesa, a few miles east of the road just south of town, is capped by Cretaceous Washita limestone. About 11 miles south, the road climbs over a low saddle in Twelve-Mile Mesa where Washita limestone crops out in roadcuts. After coming down off the saddle, the road begins a long ascent up to Sierra Madera and the Glass Mountains.

Sierra Madera (4,593 feet) is a cluster of peaks forming a dome-like structure 600 feet above the road at 11 o'clock from the Pikes Peak gas processing plant, 18 miles south of Fort Stockton. The center of the dome, 1½ miles in diameter, consists of intensely deformed and steeply dipping

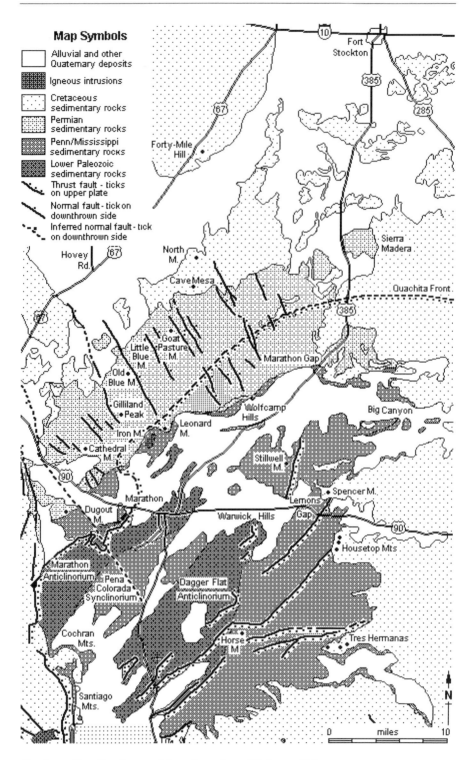

Map Symbols

- Alluvial and other Quaternary deposits
- Igneous intrusions
- Cretaceous sedimentary rocks
- Permian sedimentary rocks
- Penn/Mississippi sedimentary rocks
- Lower Paleozoic sedimentary rocks
- Thrust fault - ticks on upper plate
- Normal fault - tick on downthrown side
- Inferred normal fault - tick on downthrown side

Geology: Fort Stockton to Marathon along Highway 385

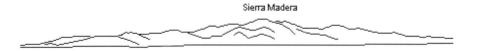

Sierra Madera from Pike's Peak gas processing plant

Permian dolomites that have been uplifted some 4,000 feet. A rim of Cretaceous strata 6 miles across surrounds the center and rises up gently towards it.

Sierra Madera has been difficult to explain. One of the early geologists to map the area, Philip King, thought it might have been produced by a hidden igneous intrusion. Later, two oil exploration wells drilled in the dome found deformed Permian strata as deep as 6,000 to 8,000 feet under the surface. Further examination proved the feature to be a bowl or funnel-shaped body, 8 miles in diameter.

Howard Wilshire of the U.S. Geological Survey and colleagues studied cone-shaped fracture zones called shatter cones and micro-breccia (rock crushed to very fine grain size) from the central structure and concluded that they must have been formed by pressures 200,000 times greater than atmospheric pressure, nearly 1,500 tons per square inch. In 1972, they proposed that Sierra Madera was an impact structure created by a meteorite striking the earth's surface in which the remains of the meteorite and the impact crater have been eroded away, leaving the underlying strata exposed. Their conclusions are now generally accepted. The age of the impact is unknown, but is less than 100 million years because Cretaceous strata were affected. The Permian strata in the center are dolomitic, more resistant to erosion than limestone, so the dome stands above the surrounding Cretaceous limestone. *Sierra Madera* is Spanish for wooded hills.

The Glass Mountains

About three miles beyond Sierra Madera, the road begins climbing a pass in the mountains through ridges of Fredericksburg and Washita limestones. Cretaceous overlies much of the Permian strata on the eastern end of the mountains; only remnants remain further west. Strata rise towards the Marathon Dome; the boundary between Washita and Fredericksburg is 1,385 feet higher here than at Fort Stockton. Good exposures of Washita limestone and marl can be seen in two rock quarries on the left near the summit of the pass and in road cuts around the picnic area at the summit (4,506 feet), 29 miles south of Fort Stockton.

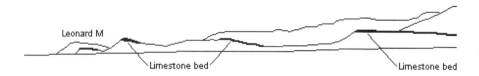

The Wolfcamp Hills: four cuestas capped by a Lenox Hills limestone bed

At the summit, the terrain levels out into low hills with heavy mainly juniper shrub cover, particularly on the north sides of the hills because rain comes mainly from the north in this area.

Permian Skinner Ranch and Hess Limestone Formations first show up at road level about a mile beyond the picnic area on the west. By the Longfellow Road intersection, 31 miles from Fort Stockton, they are on both sides of the road where they underlie Cretaceous limestones.

The Marathon Basin

Two miles from the Longfellow Road intersection, the road enters a canyon, Marathon Gap, and winds along between limestone bluffs of Cretaceous and Permian strata. A mile ahead, the road cuts through a blocky Lenox Hills limestone bed and Marathon Gap opens out into the Marathon Basin in one of the most beautiful vistas in the entire Big Bend. On the right, the Glass Mountains run southwest to Dugout Mountain. Permian strata in the mountains dip about 12 to 15 degrees to the northwest and in them erosion-resistant beds have created cuestas. The Lenox Hills limestone is the oldest and lowest of those and forms an intermittent cuesta along the Glass Mountains foothills from Marathon Gap to the Wolfcamp Hills, 10 miles ahead (photograph on page 81).

The Del Norte-Santiago Mountains are on the skyline beyond Dugout Mountain from 11 to 12 o'clock, creating a limestone escarpment 1,000 to nearly 3,000 feet high. The flat-topped Santiago Peak rises 1,000 feet above the escarpment at 11 o'clock. After a gap to the left of Santiago Mountain, the southern boundary escarpment of the basin continues east as a series of discontinuous mesas and buttes up to 1,500 feet high where Cretaceous limestones and conglomerates dip gradually away from the basin.

Four miles from Marathon Gap, 39 miles from Fort Stockton, the Dimple Hills are at 9 o'clock from the Dimple Hills Ranch entrance. In them, Dimple Limestone on the crest of an anticlinorium has been down warped. The dimples are optical illusions, the result of intersecting shallow gullies.

Cupola Butte   Dimple Hills   Sugarloaf M

The Dimple Hills and their Cretaceous mesa backdrops from the Dimple Hills Ranch entrance

The northern escarpment of the Marathon Basin is now in view on the left, forming the northern edge of Big Canyon. Big Canyon is lined on both sides by Cretaceous limestone escarpments and scattered buttes and mesas. It is the main drainage outlet from this part of the basin, running east for about 45 miles through Stockton Plateau terrain, and then turning south to eventually join the Rio Grande in Terrell County, 80 miles downstream.

Clark Butte at 7 o'clock, Ellis Butte at 8 o'clock and Cupola Butte at a little before 9 o'clock on the left flank of the Dimple Hills are capped by Trinity and in places Fredericksburg limestones over Haymond strata. The flats below are probably underlain by easily eroded Tesnus black shale. Permian strata thin along the edge of the Big Canyon escarpment on the left, disappearing completely 8 miles east of the road. No Permian strata are found south of Big Canyon; Cretaceous strata directly overlie Pennsylvanian strata there.

Sugarloaf Mountain is on the right flank of the Dimple Hills, a long outlier of Del Carmen limestone. The silvery Del Carmen escarpment at 10 o'clock contrasts with the creamy yellowish tinged Permian limestones on the right of the road. The escarpment (5,310 feet), on a tongue of Cretaceous rocks protruding into the Marathon Basin (see physiographic map on page 42), looms 500 feet above the Dimple Hills and 1,000 feet above the road.

A mile beyond the Randolph Ranch and East Kincaid Ranch entrance on the left, very broken-up Dimple Limestone crops out in a roadcut through a ridge. The bedding is vertical in some places, horizontal in other places. Another mile ahead, white Dimple Limestone beds, dipping steeply in places, are exposed in several low roadcuts. Three types of Dimple Limestone are found in the Marathon Basin. The northernmost 4 miles are near-shore limey sandstones, 250 feet thick, deposited on the ocean shelf. A second zone 4 miles across was deposited on the ocean slope, between the shelf and the ocean basin. The outcrops here are of this type. Further south, along Highway 90, turbidites crop out. They were deposited in deep water in the ocean basin, and are described in the Bullfrog Mountain – Longfellow road section.

The western escarpment from Highway 385 north of Marathon

Good views up Big Canyon can be seen from the West Kincaid Ranch entrance, 46 miles from Fort Stockton. On the other side of the road, at 4 o'clock, the Wolfcamp Hills cuestas, their escarpments facing us, dip into the base of the Glass Mountains. Lennox Hills and Neal Ranch limestones and shales cap the cuestas and are underlain by Gaptank limestones.

At the pullout on the left two miles ahead, the sizeable ridge on the skyline at 9 o'clock is the steeply dipping western limb of a Dimple Limestone syncline, which the road follows for the next 5 miles. Another Dimple Limestone hill is across the road from the Braford Ranch entrance.

At Leonard Mountain (5,872 feet), prominent at about 3 o'clock, a thick bed of Cathedral Mountain limestone caps the escarpment facing east. Skinner Ranch and Lenox Hills strata crop out on the lower slopes, overlaying Gaptank limestone at the base of the mountain (photograph on page 81). Cathedral Mountain (6,220 feet) is at 1:30 o'clock. The dark-colored, rough mountain at 2 o'clock is Iron Mountain (5,413 feet), a Tertiary trachyte intrusion. Gilliland Peak (6,520 feet), the highest point in the Glass Mountains, is on its right shoulder.

The Eastern Escarpment

Mountains on the Marathon Basin eastern escarpment are on the skyline as the road approaches Highway 90. The Housetop Mountains ridge is just before 9 o'clock. Housetop Mountain (5,460 feet) is the highest point on the ridge, about 1,500 feet above the flats below. Highway 90 crosses the escarpment at Lemons Gap just to the left of the steep-sided Gap Peak. North of the gap, the escarpment continues with Spencer Mountain (5,230 feet) and then turns east into Big Canyon. Harmon Hill (4,284 feet), the low pointed, brown hill 300 feet above the road 2 miles north of Highway 90, is an outlier of Dimple Limestone that overlies Tesnus shale.

Marathon

Settlement at Marathon began about four miles south of the present settlement at Peña Colorada Springs, the site of a military encampment, Camp Pena Colorado. The camp was set up in 1879 on the route between

Fort Clark and Fort Davis as part of the War Department's strategy to pacify the region. It was abandoned in 1893. The settlement that grew up around the post moved to its present site when the railroad was completed in 1882. It became a shipping point for ranchers in the Big Bend, and for miners at Terlingua and in Coahuila in Mexico. The 2000 Census recorded the city population at 455. Its main industries are tourism and ranching services.

Marathon Anticlinorium

The Marathon Anticlinorium first appears as a series of low hills on the right of the road at about 5 miles north of Highway 90. Highway 385 intersects the Anticlinorium just before Highway 90 in a roadcut where steeply dipping Maravillas Chert and Caballos Novaculite crop out. More novaculite crops out in a ridge above the road on the left. On the south side of Highway 90, Highway 385 continues through the anticlinorium for about 3½ miles. The first low ridges are of Alsate Shale and Fort Pena Limestone, which show up in small outcrops at roadside and on a ridge above the road on the right.

At Mile 3½, white Caballos Novaculite and black Maravillas chert and limestone are exposed in two roadcuts and on a hillside on the left of the road (photograph on page 82). The most conspicuous rock is the novaculite, a white, very fine-grained sedimentary rock similar to chert, composed of microcrystalline quartz, i.e. quartz crystals that cannot be seen under an optical microscope. Strata are intricately folded and outcrop repeatedly within the Anticlinorium (see cross section on page 43), and each time a chert or novaculite bed is repeated it forms a ridge. Chert and novaculite are very brittle and break easily into chips and small flat sections, which litter the ridges. Woods Hollow Shale, just below the Maravillas Chert in the succession (see strata table on page 39), is occasionally exposed in roadcuts. It is quite soft and seldom outcrops.

Escarpments around the Basin

Part of the pleasure of traveling around the Big Bend is in the constantly changing panoramas. The southern Marathon Basin is no exception. Except after rain, landscapes in the basin are rocky and rather drab, brown and gray the dominant colors. The surrounding limestone escarpments, constantly visible as you drive south, provide a welcome contrast, none more so than the Del Norte-Santiago Mountains to the west. They rise 1,000 to 3,000 feet above the road in a series of ridges, mesas and buttes capped by thick gray limestones that turn silvery gray in the morning sun.

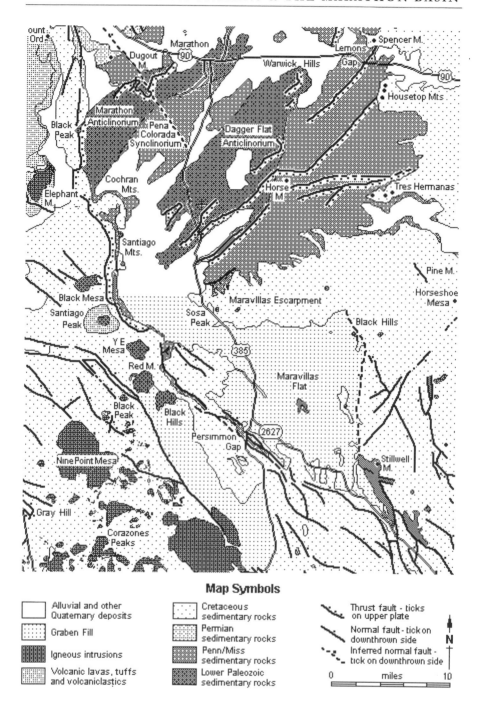

Map Symbols

☐ Alluvial and other Quaternary deposits	▨ Cretaceous sedimentary rocks	Thrust fault - ticks on upper plate
▨ Graben Fill	▨ Permian sedimentary rocks	Normal fault - tick on downthrown side
▨ Igneous intrusions	▨ Penn/Miss sedimentary rocks	Inferred normal fault - tick on downthrown side
▨ Volcanic lavas, tuffs and volcaniclastics	▨ Lower Paleozoic sedimentary rocks	

N

0   miles   10

Geology: Marathon to Persimmon Gap along Highway 385

The escarpment on the eastern boundary of the Marathon Basin is further away from the highway and less spectacular. It appears as a set of flat-topped mesas 500 to 1,500 feet above the flats below. The escarpment on the southern boundary is rather more broken up into mesas and buttes than the others. Its most easily recognized landmarks are Heart Mountain, a flat-topped butte standing high above the basin with a mesa to its left, and Sosa Peak, a sharp triangular peak to its right.

The Pena Colorada Synclinorium

The road crosses into the Pena Colorada Synclinorium just beyond the chert and novaculite roadcut 3½ miles south of Highway 90. The rocks at the surface in the synclinorium are mainly Tesnus shale and sandstone, which rarely crop out. The Wood Hollow Mountains rise out of the synclinorium on the left. They run northeast southwest and gradually converge with the road, crossing it about 12 miles south of Highway 90. They consist of tightly folded anticlines and synclines that create chert- and novaculite-crested ridges up to 500 feet above the basin floor. The first two ridges are in the synclinorium with the third and highest to its west in the Dagger Flat Anticlinorium (see cross section on page 43).

A good viewing point is about two miles past the Border Patrol inspection station, just beyond a ranch entrance on the right. The Sunshine Hills, consisting of Caballos Novaculite over Tesnus shales, are at 3 o'clock in the distance near the western edge of the synclinorium. The ridge nearest the road on the right is an anticline with white scalloped flatirons on the flank facing the road. A flatiron is a short, triangular hogback forming a ridge or spur on the flank of a hill that looks like a flatiron. A flatiron is usually a plate of steeply inclined resistant rock, in this case novaculite. At 1:30 o'clock, on East Bourland Mountain, light-colored flatirons of novaculite stand out against the dark Maravillas Chert on the higher parts of the mountain. Simpson Springs Mountain is at 1 o'clock. The whale back of Horse Mountain dominates the skyline at 9 o'clock with the Pena Blanca Mountains in the Dagger Flat Anticlinorium to its front and left.

Nine flatirons crop out on the eroded scalloped face of East Bourland Mountain at 3 o'clock from the picnic area and historical marker on the right, 10 miles south of Highway 90 (photograph on page 82). Fossilized logs have been found in the Caballos Novaculite on the northwest side of the mountain. White novaculite is conspicuous on successive ridges in the Marathon Anticlinorium on the other side of East Bourland Mountain. A good viewing point is about 150 yards beyond the picnic area, directly in line with a bed of novaculite coming towards you at 1 o'clock on the second ridge of the Simpson Springs Mountains; further ahead, you can see 26 flatirons cropping out on this ridge.

Del Norte Gap or Paso del Norte is at 2 o'clock across Maravillas Creek valley. Although dry now, the gap was probably a watercourse earlier in the landscape history; the flats on its west are 250 feet higher than on its east. To its left, the Cochran Mountains rise 1,000 feet above the plain and consist of mesas capped by flat lying Glen Rose limestones over steep dipping Haymond and Dimple strata. The Del Norte Mountains change in name to the Santiago Mountains at the Gap, although the geology remains very much the same.

The Dagger Flat Anticlinorium

The western ridge of the Dagger Flat Anticlinorium crosses the road 12 miles south of Highway 90. Steeply dipping chert and limestone beds are well exposed for about 50 yards on both sides of a roadcut in the ridge. The beds are very fine-grained, broken up, and dip steeply to the south. The road travels through the highly folded and faulted anticlinorium for the next 6 miles.

After going through two more saddles between unnamed ridges and a section of rolling hills, the road descends into the large open valley of Dagger Flat. The pullout on the left, 14½ miles south of the Highway 90 is a good place to park and view the scenery. The upper ridge-forming beds have been eroded away in Dagger Flat, leaving only scattered outcrops of the lowest and oldest formation, the intricately contorted Dagger Flat Sandstone. Some fossil fragments found in it date it to the late Cambrian, about 500 million years old. About a half-mile away on the right, two anticlines of chert and novaculite dip under the surface.

Horse Mountain (5,013 feet), another anticline, is end-on in the distance at 9 o'clock, 1,375 feet above the plain. Massive cliffs of rugged white novaculite 500 to 600 feet thick dip steeply off the anticline on its northwest face. The novaculite is thicker here than elsewhere, making it more resistant to erosion, and has created a ridge 500 feet higher than any other hill in the Marathon Basin (photograph on page 83). To the left of Horse Mountain, white novaculite cliffs can be seen on the flanks of the Peña Blanca Mountains. The mountains, on the east side of the Dagger Flat Anticlinorium, continue as white-capped broken ridges to Highway 385, which they cross obliquely about 4 miles ahead. The ridges are on the crumpled upper plate of a thrust fault, one of the many shown on the section on page 43. The upper plate has been overturned; older Caballos and Maravillas strata overlie younger Tesnus shale. Shale makes a good surface for a thrust fault. It gives way easily and contains slippery mica plates. The plate under the thrust fault is of Dagger Flat Sandstone.

The road crosses the first ridge in a saddle from which you can see a thick bed of chert and novaculite dipping steeply on both sides of the road (photographs on pages 82 and 83). Threemile Hill (4,026 feet), the highest point in the ridges, is just to the right of the road, 17 miles south of Highway 90. Large flatirons on its south side dip south at a steep angle.

A half-mile beyond Threemile Hill, two more novaculite ridges cross the road, steeply dipping and much fractured. Strata in the first ridge dip to the north and in the second to the south, showing that an anticline lies between the two. More chert beds are on the right two miles from the road.

A mile ahead, 18½ miles south of Highway 90, the road crosses the eastern edge of the Dagger Flat Anticlinorium where several chert beds are exposed in roadcuts and crosses on to Hackberry Creek flat where Tesnus shales underlie the terrain and no outcrops appear. The Tinaja Mountains (*Tinaja* is for Spanish for a large earthen jar and here refers to a natural water-collecting basin in bedrock) frame the other side of the flat, a rugged ridge with bare rock cockscomb crests. The ridge is the crumpled upper plate of a thrust fault, this one lying on Tesnus shale. The road cuts through its southwest tip, in which Caballos Novaculite dips steeply to the south.

The Basin's Southern Boundary

Once around the corner past the Tinaja Mountains, the southern boundary of the Marathon Basin comes into view, an escarpment dipping slightly to the west. The escarpment is the front of the first of three cuestas, known collectively as the Maravillas Escarpment. The low-lying country on the left between the Tinaja Mountains and the escarpment is mainly underlain by Tesnus sandstone and shale. A few thrust faults bring novaculite to the surface where it forms small ridges. Two miles ahead, 23 miles south of Highway 90, a sign points to Santiago Peak (6,521 feet). The peak is one of the most recognizable landmarks in the Big Bend, a nepheline syenite intrusion above a platform of Devil's Graveyard volcaniclastics and Cretaceous Boquillas limestone. It rises 3,400 feet above Highway 385 (see page 209 and photograph on page 84).

A good stopping point is just after the entrance to Spring Creek Ranch, 24 miles south of Highway 90. Facing us is the first Maravillas Escarpment cuesta, a section of Glen Rose strata. about 500 feet thick, composed of limestone with some marl and sandstone beds. Sandstone and conglomerate, 30 feet thick, are at its base, which lies on contorted Tesnus shales. The basal conglomerate is a distinctive reddish brown. You can see it at the base of the small butte to the right of the road ahead.

Sosa Peak (4,117 feet) is the sharp peak just left of the road. To its left, Heart Mountain (4,743 feet) is the butte-like spire with a flat-topped ridge on its left (photographs on page 84). The spire and the upper section of Sosa Peak are uncovered intrusions. Three more intrusions are behind the

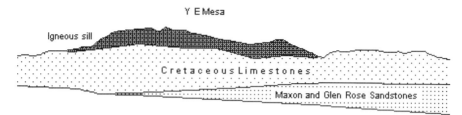

The jagged profile of Y E Mesa is visible from much of the Marathon Basin

escarpment. Intrusions erode more slowly than limestone, leaving them standing up above the limestone escarpment. Exposures of Glen Rose limestone overlying Tesnus shale continue on both sides of the road. Santiago Flats, the broad valley of Maravillas Creek, lie between the road and the Santiago Mountains.

Around the corner beyond Sosa Peak, a narrow trachyte plug (4,270 feet) rises 1,100 feet above light creamy-gray Del Carmen limestone on the left. Dark brown boulders from the plug litter its lower slopes. This Del Carmen Limestone caps the second cuesta in the Maravillas scarp, which runs 21 miles to the east, dipping south away from the Marathon Basin. The low north-facing escarpment just to the left of the plug is relatively undisturbed by the intrusion. Molten trachyte lava would have encountered the limestone at a temperature between the temperature at which limestone breaks up into calcium oxide and carbon dioxide and the temperature at which limestone melts, so some combination of those and perhaps other reactions led to the plug intruding the limestone beds without disrupting them.

A mile or so ahead, just beyond the ranch road on the left, the third cuesta in the Maravillas Escarpment, capped by Santa Elena limestone, crosses the road. A second triangle-shaped trachyte intrusion (4,076 feet) can be seen two miles away at 9 o'clock. The Santa Elena escarpment passes just in front of it not much above road level. The Santiago Mountains form a series of buttes, all about 4,500 feet high across the flat at about 4 o'clock. The igneous sill of Y E Mesa (5,384 feet) is behind them on the skyline as shown in the diagram above. A little more than halfway down to the right of the mesa, the escarpment darkens as strata change from limestone to sandstone of the Maxon Formations. The sill has preserved some Upper Cretaceous Pen strata around it. They overlie Boquillas limestones, which cap most of the escarpment.

A quarter mile ahead, going through a slight cutting of weathered limestone beds, the limestone bluffs at 9 o'clock dip only slightly to the south. The angle of dip in the Cretaceous strata decreases away from the Marathon Basin.

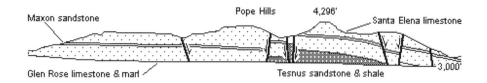

The Pope Hills from the junction of Highway 385 and FM 2627

The Black Gap Graben

At the intersection with Dove Mountain Ranch road, the broad plain of Maravillas Flat stretches 12 miles across to the Black Hills on the right. The flat is in the Black Gap Graben, the first Basin and Range structure encountered on the Fort Stockton – Persimmon Gap road. Displacement in the graben is as much as 3,000 feet at Heath Canyon, 30 miles to the south, but the floor rises to the Maravillas Escarpment, so the graben is much shallower here. Maravillas Flat is filled with gravel, which can be seen in streambeds and road banks ahead. Near the road, the gravel includes pebbles from the Caballos and Maravillas Formations, but further east it contains mainly limestone rubble. The graben is described more fully in the Persimmon Gap – Heath Canyon section of Chapter III.

On the skyline at 12 o'clock, the sharp three-pointed mountain is Pico Etereo (5,577 feet), a rhyolite intrusion in Mexico, framed by Cupola Mountain to its left and Stillwell Mountain to its right. This Stillwell Mountain is not to be confused with the Dimple Limestone ridge east of Marathon, also called Stillwell Mountain. John Stillwell was a Big Bend pioneer who began ranching around Pico Etereo in the 1880s. He had four sons, of whom Roy established a ranch at the foot of this Stillwell Mountain, where his family today runs a store, campsite and RV park (see Persimmon Gap – Heath Canyon section). Hallie Stillwell, Roy's widow, and Virginia Madison wrote a very entertaining and informative book *"How come it's called that?"* about place names in the Big Bend, reissued by Iron Mountain Press in 1997, but it does not identify the source of the Marathon Stillwell Mountain name.

The rolling brownish ridges of the Pope Hills are at 4 o'clock, two miles west of the Dove Mountain Ranch road intersection. They are made up of uplifted Cretaceous fault blocks tilted towards the road. The faults mostly run parallel to the Santiago Mountains. An extension of the Pope Hills structure, Maravillas Ridge, the cuesta whose escarpment faces the road just beyond Maravillas Creek is a monocline in Cretaceous strata, thrust faulted by Laramide-age compression and then normally faulted during Basin and Range extension. Steeply dipping limestone beds overturned by a thrust fault crop out in the streambed at the bridge over Maravillas Creek and in the ridge just south of the bridge. Younger Del Carmen beds overlie older Del Rio, Buda and Boquillas limestones, all of them dipping at about 70 degrees to the southwest. The fault runs between the Del Carmen and the lower strata.

Persimmon Gap with the Rosillos Mountains on the skyline behind it is beautifully framed at 12 o'clock from the Double Mills historic marker and pullout. Double Mills was a watering stop on the Marathon – Boquillas road. It once had two windmills, hence the name. The high peaks of the Dead Horse Mountains south of Persimmon Gap are at 11 o'clock or so, Stuarts Peak 18 miles away and Sue Peaks 22 miles away.

At the junction of FM 2627 and Highway 385, you can either continue on Highway 385 for another mile to the Big Bend National Park entrance, or turn left on to FM 2627. The latter is a very scenic 28-mile hardtop road to the Rio Grande near Heath Canyon Resort described in the next chapter. The junction is a good spot to park and view the beautiful panorama across Maravillas Flat. Just before the National Park entrance, the road begins climbing up to Persimmon Gap and provides excellent views across Maravillas Flat. Its continuation in the National Park is described in the Persimmon Gap – Panther Junction section of Chapter III.

U.S. 90 Bullfrog Mountain – Longfellow

58 Miles

This section of U.S. Highway 90 provides a different perspective from the previous section along Highway 385. It crosses the Glass Mountains and the Marathon Basin from west to east, beginning at the junction of Highways 90 and 67 on the eastern edge of the Davis Mountains volcanic field. It cuts through the southwestern tip of the Glass Mountains, providing the best views of the Glass Mountains in cross-section. It then traverses the Marathon Basin, including a long series of roadcuts near the eastern boundary of the basin in which turbidite beds of the Haymond, Tesnus and Dimple Limestone formations are beautifully exposed. It ends in Stockton Plateau canyons and mesas at the old railway stop of Longfellow, 36 miles east of Marathon, just beyond the Brewster-Pecos County line. Highway 90 continues from Longfellow through Sanderson to Del Rio and San Antonio.

Mileages are measured from the junction of Highways 90 and 67, 8 miles east of Alpine to Marathon and then from Marathon to Longfellow. Strata in the Marathon Basin and the Glass Mountains are described in the table on pages 38-9.

Bullfrog Mountain (5,400 feet) is the butte 1,000 feet above the junction of Highways 90 and 67 at 4 o'clock. It is on the west flank of the Del Norte Mountains where Crossen trachyte and Pruett and Cretaceous strata dip to the west in a near cuesta slope (see cross sections of Mount Ord on pages 216 and 220 and Bullfrog Mountain on page 233). A fault scarp faces the road on Bullfrog Mountain. The fault has a displacement of 600 feet towards the road. The low ridges on the left of Highway 90 are on its downthrown side.

Cretaceous-Permian Boundary

Because strata are dipping to the west, the road intersects older rocks as it goes east. The Cretaceous-Permian boundary on the right of the road runs up the mountains a mile east of Bullfrog Mountain. Siliceous shale,

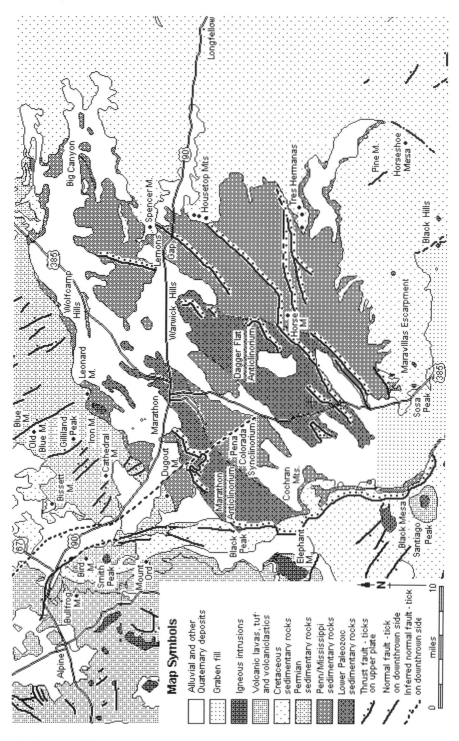

Geology: Bullfrog Mountain to Longfellow along Highway 90

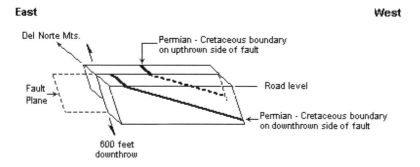

Diagram showing how fault offsets Permian-Cretaceous boundary at road level

siltstone and thin-bedded limestone of the Capitan Formation underlie the sharp hills east of the boundary. The vegetation becomes much denser because shale and siltstone create more fertile soils than Cretaceous limestones.

The boundary on the left of the road is 1¾ miles ahead in a roadcut, just beyond the Y Ranch entrance on the left. The boundary has moved east because the fault described above displaces strata along the escarpment downwards relative to strata near the road. The diagram above illustrates this effect; it is not drawn to scale.

In the roadcut, limestones of the Cretaceous Fredericksburg Group overlie Permian limestones of the Capitan Formation. There is a slight difference in the angle of the bedding in the two units but they have very similar appearances. However, the boundary between them represents a gap of 100 million years in sedimentation, an unconformity as geologists call it. The Big Bend was dry land from the end of the Permian period to the beginning of the Cretaceous period and any non-marine sedimentary rocks that might have been created were eroded away before the ocean returned. Take the time to stop and examine the outcrop. It is the only place where you can see this unconformity up close.

Bissett and Bird Mountains

Beyond the roadcut, Bissett Mountain (5,483 feet) comes into view at 9 o'clock, a dome of Fredericksburg, Bissett and Capitan strata 4 miles across. The Capitan strata have been partly replaced by iron and copper minerals and veined by large masses of calcite, indicating that a hidden igneous intrusion caused the doming. An oil exploration well drilled nearby in 1967 intersected an intrusion 4,500 feet below the surface.

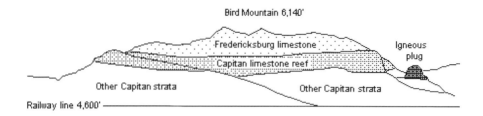

Bird Mountain rises 1,540' above the railway line.

The peak was named for Dave Bissett, a prospector who explored the site early in the twentieth century but found nothing of economic value. Parallel lines in the vegetation dip to the left high up on the mountain and in several smaller hills to the west. Some beds in the Bissett and Capitan strata are more fertile than others and support more vigorous growth.

An isolated rounded brown hill stands alone on the plain between Bissett Mountain and the road. In it, an intrusion has uplifted Word Formation sandstone.

Bird Mountain (6,140 feet), the northernmost peak of the Del Norte range, is in line with Bissett Mountain and the above intrusion at 2:30 o'clock. It is capped by 240 feet of altered Fredericksburg limestone underlain by a striking Capitan Limestone cliff, 425 feet high (photograph on page 85). The mountain has several small intrusions around its base and like Bissett Mountain, it has been a prospecting site. Galena, the ore of lead, was discovered there about 1885 by the landowner, Julius Bird. Development began around 1900 and a number of carloads of ore were shipped early in the century and again during World War II. Mining ceased after 1942 and although the property was leased to a mining company that carried out 6,000 feet of core drilling in 1981, no further operations have been attempted. The old mine workings were at the base of the beehive-shaped igneous plug on the right flank of the mountain.

Two miles beyond Bird Mountain, the sharp pyramid-shaped hill at 3 o'clock is Smith Peak (5,764 feet), a trachyte intrusion. The intrusion has domed the strata around it. Cathedral Mountain and Word strata dip at 20 degrees on the slopes to its left, their bedding planes delineated by variations in the vegetation.

The Gap in the Mountains

At Bird Mountain, Highway 90 enters a gap, 8 miles long and 2 miles wide, between the Glass Mountains on the left and the Del Norte Mountains on the right. The gap is a minor graben, a downthrown block between two normal faults.

The Mount Ord ridge with its three lava-capped mesas is visible from much of the Marathon Basin.

The fault on the right, running along the base of the Del Norte Mountains, has already been described. It displaces strata 600 feet down to the east at Bullfrog Mountain. The other, called the Altuda-Bourland Fault Zone, runs from Highway 385 near East Bourland Mountain along the north flank of Dugout Mountain. It crosses the road opposite Smith Peak and crops out in Cone and Elam Mountains north of Alpine. At its southeast end, it is a strike-slip fault, i.e. one with only horizontal movement along it, but it has about 300 feet of downthrow to the west at Elam Mountain (see page 235). Rocks break up along fault zones and water can penetrate them more easily. This leads to faster erosion than in the surrounding strata, creating canyons and eventually, as in this case, a gap. The two faults are shown on the map on page 62.

The Glass Mountains in Cross Section

Three miles ahead, about 9 miles from the Highway 67 junction, the road veers to the left and the Cretaceous mountains on the southern rim of the Marathon Basin appear in the far distance, a series of flat-topped jagged hills. The highest point on the rim is Heart Mountain, at 1 o'clock, 30 miles away. To its left, 26 miles away, the whale-backed ridge is Horse Mountain, the highest mountain in the Marathon Basin.

An unnamed ridge (5,445 feet) rises 1,000 feet above the road on the left, capped by Capitan Limestone over Word sandstones and shales. Beyond it, the wonderfully rugged east escarpment of the Glass Mountains comes into view, dominated by Cathedral Mountain (6,220 feet). (Confusingly, there is another Cathedral Mountain near Highway 118 10 miles south of Alpine). Color photographs of the escarpment are on pages 85 and 86.

The Cathedral Mountain profile demonstrates the Glass Mountains structure beautifully. Permian sedimentary rocks were tilted to the northwest 10 degrees or so before Cretaceous limestones were deposited over them. Both Permian and Cretaceous strata were tilted a further

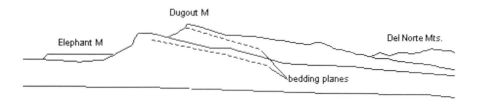

Dugout Mountain from Highway 90; an almost perfect cuesta

5 degrees by the uplift of the Marathon Dome near the end of the Cretaceous period. Compare the view here with the upper cross section on page 45. Gilliland Peak (6,520 feet), which has a similar escarpment, is on the far horizon at about 9:30 o'clock. Note how quickly the Capitan Limestone thins from Cathedral Mountain to the ridge above the road and then thickens again at Bird Mountain.

The Del Norte Mountains

Continuing past the ridge on the left, the east escarpment of the Del Norte Mountains comes into full view, jagged cliffs of light-gray limestone furrowed by sharply delineated ravines. Mount Ord (6,700 feet), the peak with the radio tower on its summit, is the highest point in the range, 2,250 feet above the road. It is on the very eastern edge of the Davis Mountains volcanic field and, like Bullfrog Mountain, is capped by Crossen trachyte which breaks off sharply to form a 600-foot cliff facing east (see its cross section on page 220). The ridge to the left is of Cretaceous Washita and Fredericksburg limestones overlying Permian Word limestones. Although you cannot see it from here, the east-facing Mount Ord escarpment continues south for 12 miles to Elephant Mountain. The two flat-topped ridges to the left of Mount Ord are part of the escarpment. The low ground in front deepens to the south and becomes Chalk Valley, 2,300 feet lower than the Mount Ord summit.

The Lenox Hills Cuesta

The second cuesta ridge in the Glass Mountains, the Lenox Hills, comes down to the road 13½ miles from the Highway 67 intersection and ends at Dugout Mountain (5,175 feet), the very prominent cuesta south of the road. The erosion-resistant beds in this cuesta are Skinner Ranch and Cathedral Mountain Formation limestones. They cap Dugout Mountain and the Lenox Hills, creating an escarpment facing southeast, and dipping gently to the northwest. Below them, Lenox Formation conglomerate overlies Pennsylvanian Gaptank limestones (see upper cross section on page 45).

The western boundary of the Marathon Basin; Lemons Gap is to the left of Gap Peak.

The U.S. Geological Survey places the epicenter of the 1995 Alpine earthquake about 4 miles north northeast of here, just below the Cathedral Mountain escarpment. The earthquake had a moderate intensity of 5.7 on the Richter scale but was the strongest to occur in West Texas since one near Valentine in 1931. It was felt as far away as San Antonio and caused rockslides on Cathedral Mountain.

The Marathon Basin from the West

A good point to stop and view the Marathon Basin from the west is at the gravel road on the south side of the road opposite the Lenox Hills and 14 miles from the junction of Highways 67 and 90. The Housetop Mountains of the basin's eastern escarpment are on the skyline at 12 o'clock as sketched above. The highest point on the skyline is Housetop Mountain (5,460 feet). Highway 90 crosses the escarpment at Lemons Gap just east of Gap Peak. On the left of Lemons Gap, the escarpment continues with Spencer Mountain (5,230 feet).

Nearer to hand, several ridges with crests of light-colored Caballos Novaculite run diagonally towards Marathon, anticlines in the Marathon Anticlinorium. The Dugout Mountain escarpment and the steep eastern face of the Lenox Hills are at 6 o'clock. Elephant Mountain (6,230 feet) is just to the left of Dugout Mountain on the horizon, an enormous flat-topped slab of nepheline syenite. The sharp pyramid-shaped hill to its left is Black Peak (4,964 feet) made up of Gaptank Formation limestone dipping at 45 degrees to the east. The flat-topped Santiago Peak is on the horizon to the left of Black Peak.

The Central Marathon Basin

Four miles ahead, 18 miles from the junction of Highway 90 and 67, upper Gaptank sandy limestone is exposed in a roadcut on the right, the only Pennsylvanian outcrop on the road. The limestone includes ammonoid and fusulinid fossils, chert pebbles and thin beds of shale and sandstone. Ammonoids had shells like those of the Pacific Nautilus but became extinct at the end of the Permian period. Fusulinids are foraminifers with cone-shaped shells about the size of wheat grains. The Gaptank Formation is the youngest Pennsylvanian formation, occurring just below the base of the Permian (see strata table on page 38).

Iron Mountain (5,413 feet) is 7 miles away on the left. The dark rough trachyte intrusion rises 900 feet above the alluvial plain at its base. Intrusions as large as Iron Mountain are rare east of the Del Norte-Santiago range. Leonard Mountain (5,872 feet), a continuation of the Lenox Hills cuesta ridge, is to the right of Iron Mountain, 2 ½ miles north. It capped by Cathedral Mountain limestone with Skinner Ranch and Lenox Hills strata on the lower slopes, and Gaptank limestone at its base. Gilliland Peak is prominent on the skyline to the left of Iron Mountain.

Two ridges in the Marathon Anticlinorium run obliquely northeast southwest across the road at the junction of Highway 90 and 385 North, one mile east of Marathon. Light-colored chert and novaculite rubble litter the crest nearest the road. Beyond them, a fine grassy plain in the Pena Colorada Synclinorium stretches to the north and east.

Four miles beyond Marathon, Harmon Hill (4,284 feet), the brown whaleback ridge at 9 o'clock, is a Dimple Limestone outcrop in the synclinorium. At 3 o'clock, Maravillas and Caballos cherts and novaculites underlie the smooth brown ridges of the Wood Hollow Mountains on the western flank of the Dagger Flat Anticlinorium.

Several low Dimple Limestone hills and ridges appear on the left across from the Lightning Ranch stock pens, 8 miles from Marathon. These exposures are on the western limb of an anticline. Stillwell Mountain, five miles ahead, is on the eastern limb of the anticline. At 3 o'clock, the northern nose of the Dagger Flat Anticlinorium disappears below the surface under Tesnus and Dimple Limestone strata in the Lightning Hills. Dark rocky Maravillas Chert beds dip steeply into the ridge on the flank nearest the road.

A little beyond the Lightning Ranch stock pens, the Shely or Tres Hermanas Mountains are at 2:30 o'clock on the skyline. The three peaks, all with summits over 5,000 feet, are on a ragged tongue of the Stockton Plateau projecting into the Marathon Basin near its southeast corner. The caprock is Maxon Sandstone. *Tres Hermanas* is Spanish for Three Sisters.

At 12½ miles from Marathon, the whale back ridge at 3 o'clock is Horse Mountain (5,013 feet), an anticline of Caballos Novaculite and Maravillas Chert. It is by far the highest mountain in the Marathon Basin, 1,375 feet above the surrounding flats. The mesas to its left on the skyline are on the southern boundary of the basin, 18 miles away. The ridges to its right, the Pena Blanca Mountains and the Warwick Hills, are on the east flank of the Dagger Flat Anticlinorium. Several anticlines have created novaculite, chert and limestone hogbacks rising above the surrounding lower ground, which is underlain by soft shales.

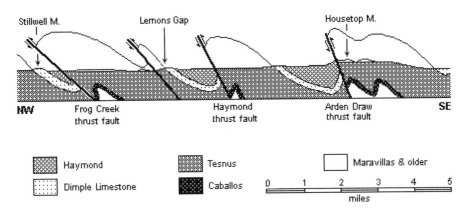

Section across the eastern Marathon Basin from Stillwell to Housetop Mountain

The East Marathon Basin

The Warwick Hills are the last outcrops of lower Paleozoic rocks along Highway 90. From this point on, Mississippian and Pennsylvanian strata are on both sides of the road. The only erosion-resistant horizon in the Mississippi-Pennsylvanian strata is the Dimple Limestone. It creates several low ridges running roughly south southwest across the terrain in front. The first such ridge is opposite the Lightning Ranch, the western limb of an anticline whose eastern limb creates Stillwell Mountain (4,623 feet), shown on the cross section above. The cross section runs southeast from Stillwell Mountain to Housetop Mountain crossing Highway 90 at Lemons Gap.

Dimple Limestone dips to the east on Stillwell Mountain, at 9 o'clock 13 miles east of Marathon. (This Stillwell Mountain is not to be confused with the other Stillwell Mountain near Persimmon Gap). The Frog Creek thrust fault is parallel to Stillwell Mountain a little to its east.

About a mile ahead, at the intersection with the old road to Haymond and Tesnus, the road enters Lemons Gap. Haymond was a small community that grew up around a station and siding on the rail line. Tesnus, 3 miles east, was another railway community. (Incidentally, its name is Sunset spelled backwards. The name Sunset was already taken for a U.S. post office). The rail line was built through the Big Bend during a period of good rainfall in the western United States. In fact, some thought that the steel rails attracted the rain. The railway companies encouraged homesteaders to buy land owned by them along their routes in the hope of increasing settlement and generating business. Settlements like Haymond and Tesnus developed around rail sidings to service the homesteaders. Haymond had mail service until 1936 and Tesnus until 1955 but both are abandoned now, commemorated only by the names of formations. Most of the homesteaders, or dryland farmers as they were called, failed to survive a severe drought that lasted from 1885 to 1891.

For the next four miles, roadcuts expose Tesnus, Dimple and Haymond marine strata intermittently. The strata are steeply dipping, having been crumpled and thrust from the southeast when South America collided with North America during the Ouachita Orogeny. Except where faulted, each formation grades into the one above without interruption. Turbidity currents created the beds in all three formations. Tesnus and Haymond sediments were derived from the southeast in South America, and Dimple sediments from the northeast in North America. Dimple sediments along Highway 90 were laid down in a deep-water basin (see page 51). In turbidite beds, the coarser grained material settles out first, the finer grained material last. In the Tesnus, for example, the lower part of each sequence is sandstone derived from sand, and the upper part shale, derived from mud. Each pair of beds represents one turbidity current. There are fifteen thousand pairs in the 3,000 feet of Haymond strata exposed along Highway 90.

The first exposure is on the left just before Lemons Gap where a small syncline has created a Dimple Limestone ridge. A half-mile beyond the Tesnus road intersection, the road veers to the right through a pass in another Dimple Limestone ridge on the west flank of an anticline (photograph on page 86). Next, the road crosses weathered thin-bedded shales and sandstone of the Haymond Formation for three-quarters of a mile or so. Haymond beds are thinner than the Tesnus beds, indicating that they were deposited further from land, fed by canyons on to a flat seabed north or west of the source of the material (photograph on page 86).

On the far side of the Haymond outcrops, the Haymond thrust fault, a zone of shattered rock 200 feet wide, crosses the road at the center of a roadcut. The fault has thrust thicker bedded Tesnus shales and sandstones over Haymond strata, cutting out the Dimple Limestone, which would normally be between the two, as shown on the cross section on page 69. The fault runs 20 miles southwest from Spencer Mountain to Horse Mountain.

In the Tesnus Formation roadcuts on the other side of the fault, thick sandstone beds are interspersed with thinner shale beds, exposed intermittently over a half-mile stretch (photograph on page 86). Earle McBride of the University of Texas believes that Tesnus sediments were laid down in a submarine fan in deep water at the toe of a river. A mile ahead, more Tesnus strata crops out in a roadcut. A half-mile further on, 18 miles from Marathon, steep Dimple limestone, mudstone and chert beds are exposed in a roadcut through a ridge, the last Paleozoic outcrop on

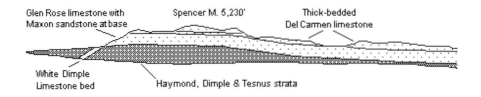

Spencer Mountain from Mile 17 east of Marathon

Highway 90 east of Marathon. This is the west limb of a syncline, the east limb of which has been cut out by the Arden thrust fault (see cross section on page 69).

The Eastern Margin of the Marathon Basin

The escarpment forming the eastern margin of the basin is on the skyline from the Lenox Hills east. The highest point in the escarpment is the Housetop Mountains range (5,460 feet), three peaks 1,250 feet above the road, capped by 200-foot cliffs of Del Carmen limestone which are underlain by 100 feet of Maxon sandstones and 300 feet of Glen Rose limestones and marls. Several thin Glen Rose limestone beds crop out on the mountain flanks (photograph on page 87).

Spencer Mountain (5,230 feet) juts into the Marathon Basin parallel to Highway 90. The mountain is 2½ mile long beginning at 9 o'clock, 16 miles from Marathon. On the flank facing the road, light-colored Del Carmen, Glen Rose and Maxon strata, similar to those on the Housetop Mountains, dip gently away from Marathon. They overlie steeply dipping Haymond, Dimple and Tesnus strata. Geologists call this an unconformity, the result of a gap in sedimentation of 142 million years, from the Haymond Formation (286 Ma) to the Cretaceous Glen Rose Formation (144 Ma). During this interval, the Paleozoic landscape was above sea level and was leveled. The Gaptank Formation is missing as well as the Permian succession. There is no evidence that they were ever deposited this far south in the eastern Marathon Basin, but if they were, they, too, were eradicated. The only outcrop you can see below the Cretaceous strata from Highway 90 is a white bed of Dimple Limestone dipping steeply on the west of the mountain as shown on the cross-section above (see also the photograph on page 87).

The ocean returned at the start of the Cretaceous period, encroaching from a deep trough near the present-day Rio Grande and lapping up against a low ridge where the Glass Mountains are now. Cretaceous limestones were laid on the level plain over the next 70 million years.

Stockton Plateau

About 19 miles from Marathon, the road enters Dry Creek Canyon with Gap Peak (5,200 feet) on the right, a butte at the northern end of the Housetop Mountains. There the road leaves the Marathon Basin and enters the Stockton Plateau physiographic province (see map on page 23). The plateau has been heavily eroded; some 50 per cent of the area is in canyon bottoms covered with alluvium. The plateau tops are of Del Carmen limestone with Glen Rose limestones and marls at road level. A broken up small butte in front of Gap Peak is the first of many demonstrations along this stretch of road of erosion creating buttes that eventually decay into pyramids and then piles of rubble.

Dry Creek Canyon narrows until it is about ½ mile wide two miles beyond Gap Peak, and the road runs between mesas capped by thick limestones for the next eight miles.

The Brewster/Pecos County line is 31 miles from Marathon Post Office. Three miles ahead, the railway line joins from the right as the road enters Sanderson Canyon. This canyon runs southeast for fifty-five miles to its mouth on the Rio Grande.

Thirty-seven miles from Marathon, the abandoned railroad station of Longfellow is on the right. Beginning in 1881 as a watering station on the Galveston, Harrisburg, and San Antonio Railway and named for the poet Longfellow, it became a livestock shipping point for a wide area. A railroad depot, telegraph office and ballast quarry were soon established. A post office opened in 1890. The settlement became headquarters for the Longfellow Ranch. As better highways were built in the twentieth century, however, Longfellow lost much of its business to larger towns. The post office was closed down in 1933. The railroad closed its freight and telegraph office in 1944. The water column and well facilities were abandoned in 1954 when diesel engines came into use. Today, only the ranch buildings and the ruins of some of the old railroad structures remain.

From Longfellow you can return to Marathon or continue on Highway 90 to Sanderson, 17 miles ahead. From Sanderson you can go north to Interstate 10 or continue on Highway 90 to Del Rio and San Antonio.

III Down by the River

The Big Bend is at its most dramatic down by the Rio Grande, the area south of a line from Persimmon Gap to the Solitario. It includes all 800,000 acres of Big Bend National Park, the western part of the Black Gap Wildlife Management Area and a slice of the Big Bend Ranch State Park, all open to public access. There are the two large mountain ranges, the Dead Horse and the Chisos Mountains, as well as many individual peaks. Also included are substantial sections of low-lying soft sedimentary rocks, some dissected into colorful badlands, and the broad valley of the Rio Grande on its southern boundary.

The Chihuahua Trough

The geological record of the area down by the Rio Grande begins late in the Jurassic period, around 175 million year ago, when a trough formed from El Paso to west of Presidio. The trough, known to geologists as the Chihuahua Trough, was a rift inland from the edge of the continent, which at that time ran from about Lajitas northeast across the area. The trough continued to sink during the Triassic and the Lower Cretaceous periods, accumulating 12,000 to 25,000 feet of marine sediments. As a result, Lower Cretaceous strata today thicken from about 1,100 feet at the southern margin of the Marathon Basin to 2,100 feet at Dog Canyon and 3,900 feet at the Rio Grande.

The Laramide Orogeny

The Laramide Orogeny began in the Big Bend around 70 Ma and was completed by 50 Ma. During the orogeny, the earth's crust was compressed from east and west, leading to the creation of uplifts and basins. The main Laramide mountain range runs south of the Rio Grande

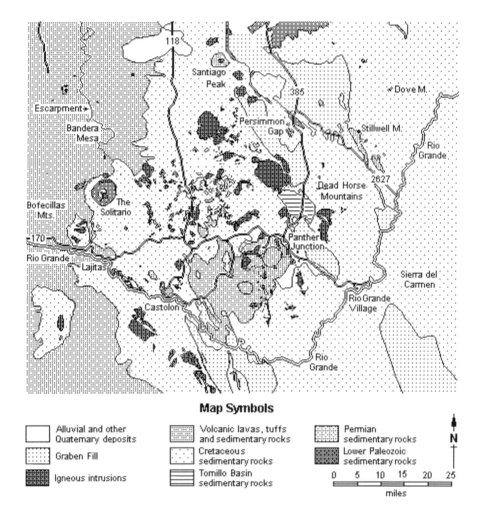

Map Symbols

Alluvial and other Quaternary deposits	Volcanic lavas, tuffs and sedimentary rocks	Permian sedimentary rocks
Graben Fill	Cretaceous sedimentary rocks	Lower Paleozoic sedimentary rocks
Igneous intrusions	Tomillo Basin sedimentary rocks	0 5 10 15 20 25 miles

Geology down by the Rio Grande

from El Paso to Lajitas and then turns south to become the Sierra Madre Oriental. Several mountains and uplifts were created east of the main range, including the Del Norte-Santiago-Dead Horse Mountains and the Marathon Dome.

The Tornillo Basin and the Disappearance of Dinosaurs

The Tornillo Basin began forming between the main range and the Del Norte-Santiago-Dead Horse Mountains at the end of Aguja sedimentation, 70 Ma. Early Aguja sedimentary rocks were marine sandstones and shales laid down in a shallow sea not far from the coast. Neither the mountains we see now nor the Rio Grande existed then. The sea withdrew across the area at 75 Ma, leaving behind flat-lying flood plains though which rivers and streams meandered and all Tornillo Basin strata were laid down in this setting, as sandstones in river or stream channels, and as mudstones or shales on the flood plains. It must have been rather like the Mississippi delta is today, with enormous trees and lush vegetation growing on the banks of slow-moving rivers and streams. Aguja sediment grains were mainly of volcanic origin and probably came from the Sierra Madre Occidental to the west.

Once the area became dry land, plant-eating dinosaurs such as duck-billed hadrosaurs, horned ceratopsians, anklyosaurs and theropods moved into the Big Bend from the north and their fossil remains have been widely excavated over the past 75 years. Other reptile fossils found in Aguja rocks include the giant crocodile *Deinosuchus,* which lived in marshy openings in the forest. Jawbone fragments and teeth of swimming reptiles are also present and pterosaur fossils have been found, including those of one that is believed to have had a wingspan of 36 feet. Its replica, *Quetzalcoatlus northropi,* is on display at the Park Headquarters.

The Javelina Formation which followed the Aguja Formation from 70 to 66 Ma consists mainly of mudstone with sandstone lenses, and with vividly colored yellowish gray and reddish gray horizons. The colored horizons are fossil soils; the yellow and red horizons come from iron concentrations. You can see them in Tornillo Flat and along Highway 118 from the Park entrance to Study Butte. Soils only develop in well-drained terrain; drainage improved in the basin during the Javelina time as Laramide mountains began to rise. The climate at the time was somewhat humid and arid. The grains in the strata were still of volcanic origin, from Cretaceous volcanoes in Mexico or Arizona.

More dinosaurs arrived during the Javelina, most prominently the Alamosaurus, a long-necked, long-tailed giant sauropod. Sauropods, the largest animals ever to walk the earth, had been a highly successful group

Period Name	Age m.y.	Formation	Description
Pleistocene	1.6-0.1	Old Quaternary	Consolidated high-level terrace gravel, pediment gravel, and valley-fill deposits.
Pliocene - Miocene	24-1.6	Fingers	Conglomerate and sandstone, poorly consolidated; up to 700 ft. thick; age 2½ Ma at base.
		Estufa Canyon	Three alluvial fan deposits, upper 1,000 ft, of similar age to Fingers Formation, 2 Ma; oldest ~ 10 Ma; 1,450-1,700 ft. thick.
		Delaho	Upper member, sandstone and conglomerate; up to 1,100 ft. thick. Lower member, mostly sandy siltstone; about 1,100 ft. thick; age 23 Ma at base.
Oligocene	34-24	South Rim	Mainly rhyolitic pyroclastic flows with named units described below in and south of Chisos Mountains; age 33-29 Ma.
			Burro Mesa Member: sodium-rich rhyolitic welded pyroclastic flow with quartz phenocrysts, gray; 400-500 ft. thick, age ~ 29 Ma.
			Lost Mine Member: reddish porphyritic rhyolitic ash-flow tuff, local lava flows; mainly within Pine Canyon caldera.
			Wasp Spring Member: poorly to, in places, densely welded pyroclastic flow breccia and rhyolite; 100-350 ft. thick.
			Pine Canyon Rhyolite: ash-flow tuff, up to 800 ft. thick.
Eocene and Oligocene	58-24	Chisos	In high Chisos Mountains: 2,000 feet of mostly fine tuffaceous sandstone in 1- to 2-foot beds followed by 1,500 feet of mostly gray coarse sandstone with beds and lenses of tuffaceous claystone, sandstone and conglomerate.
			In south and west of high mountains: up to 2,500 ft. of claystone, mudstone and sandstone, tuffaceous in places, tuff, thick conglomerate lenses, some freshwater limestone, with lavas and ash-flow tuff interbedded; named members:
			Tule Mountain Member: porphyritic trachyandesite, spotted gray to brownish gray, weathers brown to reddish brown; up to 350 ft. thick; age ~34 m.y.
			Mule Ear Spring Member: poorly consolidated to very hard, brittle, silicified ash-flow tuff, various shades of pink and red; weathers brown; contains Oligocene vertebrate fossils; 8-12 ft. thick; age ~34 m.y.
			Bee Mountain Member: fine- to medium-grained porphyritic basalt, several flows; 25-80 ft. thick in Chisos Mts., 527 ft. thick at Cerro Castellan; age ~34 m.y.
			Ash Spring Member: two or more porphyritic basalt flows; up to 200 ft. thick; age ~ 44.5 m.y.
			Alamo Creek Member: fine-grained, hard, dark basalt; 20-208 ft. thick; age ~ 46 m.y.
Eocene	58-37	Canoe	Claystone, tuffaceous claystone, mudstone, sandstone, conglomeratic sandstone, calcareous tuff, silicified tuff, some basalt flows up to 60 ft. thick; up to 1,200 ft. thick.
		Hannold Hill	Mostly claystone, gray and maroon, some sandstone and channel conglomerate, gray, brownish gray and grayish white; up to 850 ft. thick; Exhibit Sandstone Member, 12-15 ft. thick 320 ft. above base, contains vertebrate fossils; age 56-51 Ma.

Period Name	Age m.y.	Formation	Description
		Black Peaks	Sandstone at base, conglomeratic, gray to grayish white; mudstone, mottled gray and deep dark-red; vertebrate fossils common; 284-866 ft. thick; age 65-56 Ma.
Upper Cretaceous	98-66	Javelina	Claystone and sandstone; claystone, bentonitic, dull gray, olive green, deep dark red, dirty brown, weathers into rounded topographic forms; sandstone, lenticular bodies, vertebrate fossils and petrified wood common; 244-936 ft. thick.
		Aguja	Claystone, sandstone and lignite. Upper part continental deposits up to 880 ft. thick; sandstone, argillaceous, various shades of yellow and brown; claystone, calcareous in part, greenish gray to yellowish brown and purple; a few lignite beds; vertebrate fossils, petrified wood common.
			Lower part 3 units; first transitional from upper unit; middle unit, silty to sandy claystone, medium to dark gray, weathers yellow to yellowish brown, marine fossils common; 175-500 ft. thick; lower unit sandstone, conglomeratic at base, indurated, yellowish gray to yellowish brown; 5-35 ft. thick.
		Pen	Mostly claystone; upper part sandy; middle part, yellow scattered sandy beds; lower 50 ft. calcareous claystone with inch-thick chalk beds, light bluish gray, weathers yellow to yellowish gray; marine fossils throughout; 219-700 ft. thick.
		Boquillas	*San Vicente Member*: limestone flags, interbedded with gray to yellowish gray platy marl and soft gray marl; marine fossils abundant; 130-400 ft. thick.
			Ernst Member: limestone, siltstone and claystone; limestone, silty, flaggy, beds mostly 2-5 ins., some up to 18 ins.; bluish gray, weathers light yellowish gray to light brownish yellow, blocky from joints; marine fossils abundant; 450 ft. thick.
Lower Cretaceous	144-98	Buda	Limestone, grayish white; 25 ft. thick at Santa Elena Canyon.
		Del Rio Clay	Mostly claystone, some interbedded limestone and sandstone; claystone, soft, bluish to greenish gray, weathers yellow to light brown; 30 ft. thick at Santa Elena Canyon.
		Santa Elena Limestone	Fine grained to microgranular, massive, beds up to 10-ft. thick, light gray to white; weathers dark gray and shades of brown; forms cliffs; about 740 ft. thick at Santa Elena Canyon.
		Sue Peaks	Yellowish shale, yellowish-gray marl and yellowish-gray and gray thin-bedded nodular limestone; forms slope between Santa Elena and Del Carmen limestones; 265 ft. thick at Santa Elena Canyon.
		Del Carmen	Limestone, microgranular to fine-grained, massive, gray, weathers shades of dark brown, yellowish brown, and pinkish brown; forms sheer escarpments; 150 ft. thick at Santa Elena Canyon.
		Telephone Canyon	Limestone, nodular, marly, yellowish brown to brownish gray, yellowish marl partings; marine megafossils common; forms slope at base of Del Carmen Limestone cliffs; about 25 ft. thick at Santa Elena Canyon.
		Glen Rose	Alternating resistant limestone ridges and soft marls which weather to form stairstep topography; upper 30 ft. exposed at Santa Elena Canyon.

of animals in earlier times, but by Javelina time Alamosaurus was the only sauropod remaining in North America. Adults were probably 60 feet long and weighed around 35 tons. Recently, paleontologists from the University of Texas at Dallas excavated a bone bed in the Javelina Formation at Tornillo Flat containing the remains of an adult and two half-grown Alamosaurus dinosaurs. Alamosaurus is named after a spring, Ojo Alamo, south of Farmington, New Mexico where it was first discovered.

The end of the Javelina, 66 Ma, marks the boundary between the Cretaceous and the Tertiary periods, the K/T boundary as it is called (K is geology shorthand for Cretaceous), a time when a mass extinction of living creatures occurred; about 50 per cent of all species disappeared, including pterosaurs and dinosaurs. Crocodiles were severely affected but recovered. Birds survived although their theropod relatives died out. Turtles survived, as did snakes, lizards and amphibians.

The mysterious extinction of dinosaurs, the most successful group of animals on earth for 150 million years, has attracted much scientific and popular attention. Scientific interest was boosted when a clay layer at the K/T boundary in Italy was found in 1980 to have a higher than expected content of iridium. Similar anomalies were found in several other parts of the earth. Iridium is an element only found in high concentrations in extraterrestrial bodies. The geologist Walter Alvarez of Stanford University and his father Louis Alvarez, the Nobel-prize winning physicist, proposed in 1992 that a meteorite had collided with the earth. This impact would have generated an enormous cloud of debris, which would have gone up into the atmosphere and reduced the sunlight reaching the earth. This in turn would have diminished plant life and hence feed for the dinosaurs and other victims. The debris would have come back to earth eventually and created the clay layer with the elevated iridium content.

A likely impact site, the Chicxulub Crater, 100 miles in diameter, was discovered in 1992 deeply buried in the Yucatan Peninsula, about 1,200 miles south west of the Big Bend. A worldwide search for other craters has turned up two of a similar age, one in the Ukraine, the other in the North Sea, leading some geologists to propose that several impacts took place over a period of time rather than instantaneously as proposed in 1992. Walter Alvarez wrote a best selling book on the subject, *T Rex and the Crater of Doom.*

No iridium-rich layer has been found at the K/T boundary in the Big Bend as yet. It may have been washed away by flooding, however, a very common occurrence in soft riverbank sedimentary rocks. The Big Bend climate changed at K/T boundary to one that was cooler and wetter than before; rainfall doubled from perhaps 36 to 72 inches per year. The change took place suddenly just above the highest point where dinosaur bones have been found, and lasted for 2 million years. Incidentally, the oldest

Tertiary mammal fossil found in the National Park is 35 feet above the youngest dinosaur fossil found, equivalent to about 235,000 years at the average rate of sediment formation.

Lower Black Peaks strata, 66 to 62 Ma in age, like the Javelina strata below them, have striking color banding from soils developing in the cooler, more humid climate. Upper Black Peaks strata, 62 to 56 Ma, were deposited more quickly than before and fewer fossil soils or paleosols were developed. The sediment grains in Black Peaks strata were still mainly of volcanic origin. Hannold Hill strata, 56 to 51 Ma, were also deposited quickly, and are mainly mudstones derived more from adjacent Cretaceous rocks and less from distant volcanic rocks. The lower Canoe Formation in Tornillo Flat, 51 to 48 Ma in age, and its equivalent, the lower Devil's Graveyard Formation west of the National Park, were deposited quite slowly, at perhaps 45 feet per million years, and are mainly sandstones derived from nearby Cretaceous limestones.

The upper Canoe Formation sequence in Tornillo Flat and the equivalent lower and middle Devil's Graveyard Formation in the west, 48 to 46 Ma, were mostly volcanic and not stream deposits, derived at least partly from local volcanoes in the Christmas Mountains. They represent a transition to the overlying volcanic-derived Chisos Formation strata described below.

Laramide Mountains and Uplifts

Sediments were deposited in the Tornillo Basin faster during periods of active mountain building than during quiet periods. Study of these rates shows that there were two main mountain building periods, 70 to 66 Ma during the Javelina Formation period, and 59 to 51 Ma, during the upper Black Peaks and Hannold Hill Formations periods. The Santiago-Dead Horse Mountains are the most important Laramide structure down by the river. The Santiago section of the range, a narrow overturned fold on the northeast flank of the Tornillo Basin, has been described in Chapter II. It changes in name to the Dead Horse Mountains at Dog Canyon, about 5 miles south of Persimmon Gap. The character changes, too, from a ridge less than a mile wide to a broad uplift, 14 miles wide, with a series of monoclines along its crest and western flanks, and tilted fault blocks in its eastern half. The greater width of the mountains south of Dog Canyon is thought to be due to the greater thickness of Cretaceous sedimentary rocks towards the Rio Grande and the Chihuahua Trough.

Two sets of faults were created in the Dead Horse range during the Laramide Orogeny, one trending north-northwest and the other west-northwest. When the earth's crust began to be extended at the onset of Basin and Range activity, 25 million years later, some of these old

Laramide faults were pulled apart and narrow grabens developed between the blocks. In other places, the faults were opened out by erosion. In either case, diamond-shaped blocks were created and separated by steep, narrow canyons. They are particularly noticeable along FM 2627 on the east side of the range. Monoclines form prominent ridges on the west side of the range, such as the one from Stuarts Peak to the Sue Peaks, 3,000 feet above Tornillo Flat.

Other Laramide structures created down by the river perhaps includes the Terlingua Uplift, although this is disputed by some geologists, and a series of anticlines and domes which trend northwest across the area from the Rio Grande to the Christmas Mountains. The latter series begins at the river where Mariscal and San Vicente Mountains are anticlines that straddle the river. Strata have been elevated 2,500 feet by the Mariscal Mountain anticline, shown on the map on page 98 as crossing the river at Mariscal Canyon.

Along the trend, strata under the Chisos Mountains were uplifted into an elongated dome striking north-northwest and further uplifted by later igneous activity. The dome's full height is unknown; its summit is buried under Chisos Formation rocks. However, the Javelina-Aguja boundary is about 1,000 feet higher at the base of the Chisos Mountains than in the Rio Grande valley, so the dome was at least that high.

In the Christmas Mountains, Cretaceous strata are draped across the top of a dome. Again, some of this is due to Laramide folding and some due to a later intrusion, but how much to each is unknown.

The Chisos and South Rim Formations

The Chisos Formation in the higher Chisos Mountains and down below the South Rim differs from that south and west of the mountains. In the high Chisos Mountains, the strata are mostly of volcaniclastic material derived from ash, with occasional interbedded basalt lavas. Some of the early ash deposits came from calderas in the Christmas Mountains, which began erupting about 45 Ma while other ash deposits came from Mexico. The formation has a maximum thickness of 3,500 feet at Pummel Peak above the Park Headquarters and follows the Canoe Formation without interruption.

To the south and west of the high mountains, the Chisos Formation consists mainly of pyroclastic flows and lavas that are more siliceous and are interbedded with various thicknesses of claystone, mudstones and sandstones, tuffaceous in places, tuff, conglomerate and some freshwater limestone. The maximum thickness recorded is 2,400 feet at Tule Mountain.

Fifty million years ago, the Marathon dome rose some 3,500 feet above Marathon. Today, the most complete section of the dome remaining is in the Glass Mountains on the left. The above photograph, taken at Marathon Gap, shows strata on the northwest flank of the dome. The Wolfcamp Hills, the series of cuestas midway down the face, are capped by Permian Lenox Hills Limestone.

From the left, Iron, Cathedral and Leonard Mountains are seen from 40 miles south of Fort Stockton on Highway 385. Iron Mountain is a trachyte intrusion. Leonard Mountain is the highest summit on the middle cuesta ridge in the Glass Mountains, capped by Cathedral Mountain limestone. Cathedral Mountain is part of the highest cuesta ridge. It is capped by limestone of the Capitan Formation.

The Caballos Novaculite, a hard silica rock, creates most of the ridges and other hills in the Marathon Basin. The photograph on the left is from a roadcut in Highway 385 3 miles south of Marathon in which individual beds are quite thin. The right photograph is of a novaculite exposure in a roadcut at Threemile Hill, 22 miles south of Marathon, in which individual beds are thicker.

The Caballos Novaculite is most spectacularly displayed as flatirons, seen here on East Bourland Mountain, 8.5 miles south of Marathon. A flatiron develops when a resistant bed on the flank of a mountain is eroded into scallops, called flatirons because of their shape.

In this photograph to the left of Highway 385 on Dagger Flat, 13 miles south of Marathon, we look across the axis of an anticline to Horse Mountain, the highest point in the Marathon Basin. Caballos Novaculite, 500 to 600 feet thick is draped by the anticline over the summit, underlain by Maravillas Chert. One of the Tres Hermanas peaks is on the right, 10 miles away.

This photograph looks up the axis of the Horse Mountain anticline on the left of Highway 385 17 miles south of Marathon. The ridge in the near left is a hogback, a cuesta in which the beds dip steeply on the dip slope side, so that the crest of the ridge is sharp, like a hogback. On the right, the same bed dips towards the camera. Eventually, overlying strata will erode off and it will form a flatiron.

Santiago Peak is one of the most recognizable and visible landmarks in the Big Bend. Its upper 1,250 feet is a nepheline syenite plug overlying 900 feet of sandstones and tuffs of the Devil's Graveyard Formation and 450 feet of Cretaceous Boquillas lime- stones and marls (see the cross-section on page 209). The intrusion has slowed down erosion of the sediments.

Sosa Peak on the left and Heart Mountain on the right are on the south margin of the Marathon Basin, 21 miles south of Marathon on Highway 385. Both are cored by tra- chyte intrusions. In Heart Mountain, the intrusion has created a butte standing up above a mesa on its left. In both photographs, you can see Cretaceous Maxon strata dipping away at a low angle from the Marathon Dome.

Bird Mountain, seen here from Highway 90 5 miles east of the junction of Highways 67 and 90, is capped by 240 feet of Cretaceous limestone underlain by a striking Capitan Limestone cliff, 425 feet high. Partly hidden intrusions have domed strata in the mountain and made them harder than usual, and account for the mountain's prominence.

The magnificent east face of Cathedral Mountain, photographed from Highway 90 10 miles east of the junction of Highways 67 and 90, is capped by Permian Capitan Formation limestone, a fossil sponge reef. The reef covers most of the western slope of the Glass Mountains, dipping away from the Marathon Dome. It is named after Capitan Peak, the highest mountain in Texas.

On the left, Cathedral Mountain is in profile, 9 miles east of the junction of Highways 67 and 90. On the right, turbidite beds of the Tesnus Formation are exposed in a roadcut 17 miles east of Marathon on Highway 90. Tesnus strata along Highway 90 are from the upper part of the formation and consist of thick beds of sandstone and shale.

The Dimple Limestone Formation on the left, photographed in a roadcut on Highway 90 15 miles east of Marathon, here consists of limestones, mudstones and chert beds deposited in a ocean basin from a source to the west. On the right, Haymond Formation beds of sandstone grading into shale are seen in a roadcut 15.7 miles east of Marathon. Each bed was laid down by a turbidity current.

On Spencer Mountain, photographed from the historical marker 16 miles east of Marathon, horizontal beds of Cretaceous Del Carmen, Maxon and Glen Rose strata can be seen cropping out in the upper third of the mountain. Nearly vertical beds of the Haymond, Dimple and Tesnus Formations overlie the lower part of the mountain and rarely crop out (drawing on page 71).

The Housetop Mountains are on the eastern boundary of the Marathon Basin south of Highway 90. They have a similar sequence of strata to Spencer Mountain. The highest point, Housetop Mountain, is on the right. This photograph was taken from 15 miles east of Marathon.

Dove Mountain on the left, photographed from Mile 8.5 on FM 2627, is one of the rare sizable igneous intrusions east of the Santiago Mountains. Santa Elena limestone on the right, seen in a roadcut at Mile 5 on FM 2627, is the main erosion-resistant limestone in the Big Bend, capping the Dead Horse Mountains, Mesa de Anguila, the Terlingua Uplift and many others.

Stillwell Mountain, photographed from Mile 11.4 on FM 2627, is built up of basalt lava flows dipping away from the camera into a syncline. Basalt is composed mainly of iron- and magnesium-rich minerals and is dark compared to limestone. Several of the lava flows crop out in the mountain face.

Stairway Mountain, photographed from Mile 11.6 on FM 2627, is a tilted fault block of Cretaceous limestones. The boundary fault of the Black Gap graben runs along the base of mountain, dropping strata about 2,000 feet towards the camera. Santa Elena and Sue Peaks limestone beds have eroded to create a distinctive stairstep-like profile, 1,525 feet high (diagram on page 104).

The Black Gap, a pass in the basalt ridge, is seen from the entrance to Black Gap Wildlife Management Area Headquarters at Mile 17 on FM 2627. The high fault scarp of Cupola Mountain behind it is on the eastern boundary of the Black Gap Graben. The cupola of Cupola Mountain, a dark basalt remnant, on the left of the escarpment, is 2,000 feet above the valley of Maravillas Creek below.

These spectacular high buttresses of Santa Elena Limestone are on Sierra Larga in the Dead Horse Mountains, on the left at Parking Area 7, Mile 22.4 on FM 2627. They are between 2,200 to 2500 feet above the road.

The beautiful Pico Etereo is on the skyline intermittently from Persimmon Gap to Heath Crossing. The peak is a rhyolite intrusion 20 miles across the border in Mexico. The fluorspar that once was trucked up FM 2627 to Marathon was mined mainly around Pico Etereo. Mining continues in the area but now supplies only the Mexican market.

Persimmon Peak, photographed from the summit of Persimmon Gap at the entrance to Big Bend National Park, shows off the complex Santiago Mountains to fine effect. The cross-section on page 110 explains the structure.

The upper part of the Rosillos Mountains, seen here from 16 miles north of Panther Junction, is a granite and rhyolite laccolith. Its base is just above the line of light-colored tuff outcrops on a scarp of the Chalk Draw Fault. The low hills nearest the camera are a continuation of the intrusion, downthrown towards the camera by the fault.

The Persimmon Gap – Panther Junction road crosses on to Tertiary from Cretaceous sedimentary rocks at about Mile 13 from Panther Junction. The oldest Tertiary formation is the Black Peaks Formation here seen as purplish gravels cropping out on the left at Mile 9, overlain by an irregular bed of Hannold Hill sandstone, the next oldest formation.

Hannold Hill sandstones have been eroded into more elaborate pillars on the left just beyond the bridge over Tornillo Creek at Mile 8 from Panther Junction. Such pillars are called hoodoos in the southwest. The Chisos Mountains loom in the background.

On the left, Canoe Formation tuffaceous claystone crops out at the base of Hannold Hill, 5 miles north of Panther Junction. The Canoe Formation grades upwards into Chisos Formation tuffs in the eastern National Park. On the right, gravels of the eastern Chisos Mountains pediment are exposed in a roadcut on Hannold Hill.

The approach to Panther Junction is dominated by the Chisos Mountains rising above the junction. Wright Mountain on the left and Panther Peak on the right are on the rim of the Pine Canyon Caldera. Both peaks are crested by rhyolitic eruptions of the South Rim Formation. The valley between them, Smugglers Gap, leads to Lost Mine Peak in the background, also on the caldera rim.

This is a view of the full Chisos Mountains, taken from Mile 16 on the Rio Grande Village road south of Panther Junction. The peaks seen are shown on the outline on page 124. All are capped by South Rim lavas and pyroclastic rocks, overlying Chisos Formation tuffs and lavas.

The magnificent 3,600-feet escarpment of Sierra el Carmen across the Rio Grande in Mexico is seen here from near Dugout Wells Road, 6 miles from Panther Junction. To its right, the high peaks of the Sierra del Carmen, 40 miles away and up to 8,900 feet high, are capped by volcanic flows similar to those in the Chisos Mountains.

The village of Boquillas del Carmen and the Rio Grande valley is seen from the Boquillas Canyon Overlook 2 miles west of the canyon. The machinery above the river was used at one time to process and store fluorite mined nearby for export to the United States.

Boquillas Canyon runs from top left to mid-right in this view from the Boquillas Canyon Overlook, 2 miles west of the canyon. In front, limestone blocks on either side of the canyon tilt towards the canyon. Behind them, the large block on the right of the canyon is slightly tilted towards the canyon. Pico Cerda or Schott Tower, the highest point on the Sierra el Carmen, is on the horizon at right.

96

This photograph of the mouth of Boquillas Canyon, taken from the river bank, shows one branch of the Boquillas Canyon Fault in the right cliff. Strata are down thrown about 600 feet to the right by this fault.

In Tornillo Creek valley, seen from Mile 2 on the Panther Junction – Study Butte road, the creek runs along the light-colored Cretaceous Aguja and Javelina badlands in front of the Rosillos Mountains. Santiago Peak is on the skyline at the far left, 35 miles away.

The lavas had multiple sources: the Mule Ear Spring ash-flow tuff was erupted from the Sierra Quemada caldera, on the southwest flank of the Chisos Mountains; the Tule Mountain member may have had a source in the Sierra Rica caldera in Mexico as well as sources in the National Park.

After a hiatus, during which rising magma domed the Chisos strata, a series of pyroclastic flows of the South Rim Formation erupted between 31.7 and 32.9 Ma from the Pine Canyon caldera and from vents just outside the caldera on to the surface of the eroded Chisos Formation. The outside vents ended by creating the beautiful lava domes of Casa Grande, Toll Mountain and Emory Peak. The caldera is perched on the northeast corner of the Chisos Mountains, with Pummel, Wright and Panther Peaks on its rim directly overlooking Panther Junction.

Further west, along a 10-mile zone from Burro Mesa to Castolon, similar pyroclastic flows erupted from a series of vents on Burro Mesa, Kit Mountain, Goat Mountain and Cerro Castellan. Here, however, volcanic activity seems to have lasted longer. The youngest lava, the Burro Mesa rhyolite, is dated at 29 Ma.

The Chisos Mountains Pluton

Igneous activity in the high Chisos Mountains closed with the intrusion of a large granite and quartz syenite pluton, the Chisos Mountains pluton, just west of the Pine Canyon caldera. It has a very similar composition to the South Rim pyroclastic flows, although slightly younger, and almost certainly came from the same source. The intrusion dragged up Aguja, Pen and Boquillas sedimentary rocks with it. They crop out in the Chisos Basin, more than 2,000 feet above their normal position.

Basin and Range Structures

At about 28 Ma, near the end of volcanic activities in the National Park and environs, the earth's crust began to be stretched across the Big Bend with blocks dropping down along normal faults into the additional width created by this extension, resulting basins or *grabens* in geological parlance. Blocks not dropped down became mountain ranges or *horsts*. Normal faults mainly run northwest to southeast, although later ones tend to run north south.

The main structures down by the river are shown on the map on the following page. The largest structure is the Sunken Block, an enormous graben, 45 miles across. Its southwest boundary is the Terlingua Fault which displaces strata 2,900 feet into the block at the mouth of Santa Elena Canyon. Its northeast boundary is a set of faults along the western flanks of the Santiago and Dead Horse Mountains, the latter stepping

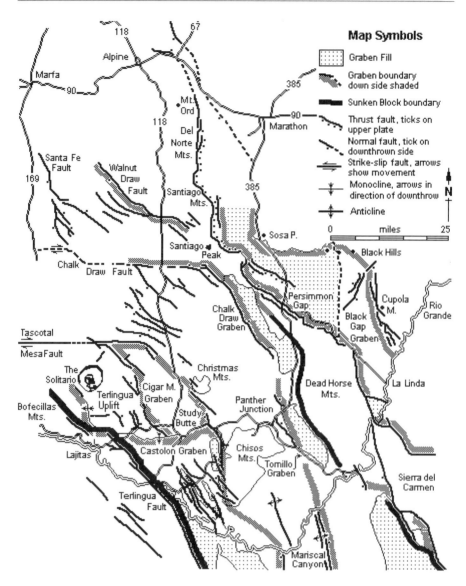

Major structures in the Big Bend

eastward as you go south into Mexico. Displacement is about 2,000 feet in Tornillo Flat at the foot of the Dead Horse range. The block deepens in Mexico: the highest fault scarp in the Sierra del Carmen is almost 6,000 feet while the Terlingua Fault displacement increases to 4,500 feet 10 miles south of the border.

Faults developed parallel to the bounding faults along the edges of the Block, creating the grabens shown on the map, the Chalk Draw, Tornillo,

Castolon and Cigar Mountain Grabens. These faults generally have displacements of at most 1,500 feet. Belts of parallel faults developed southwest of the Chisos Mountains horst and the northwest of the Christmas Mountains horst. In some places, monoclines developed instead of faults, as at the southern and western margins of the Terlingua Uplift, and along the foothills of the Santiago Mountains north of Persimmon Gap. The Black Gap Graben is outside the Sunken Block, between the Santiago-Dead Horse range and the Cupola Mountain highlands. Its floor has been dropped 3,000 feet near the Rio Grande. The graben has been partly filled with Black Gap Basalt, 22 million years old, proving it to be one of the older grabens in the area. A few minor grabens occur north of the Sunken Block, one between the Chalk Draw and Walnut Draw Faults; another probably of Basin and Range age crosses Highway 90 north of Mount Ord.

Although it began 28 million years ago, most of the Basin and Range movement has taken place in the last 10 million years. It continues to the present day; recently formed fault escarpments are found in the Big Bend and earthquakes from continuing fault movement occur occasionally, the most recent one near Marathon in 1995.

Erosion down by the River

The most recent episode in the geological history down by the river is the development of the Rio Grande and erosion associated with it (see page 32). Most of the erosion seems to have taken place in the last 2½ million years. The Fingers Formation conglomerate of that age is found at up to 4,000 feet elevation on Burro Mesa. Similar deposits occur up to 4,600 feet in Madera Canyon, 20 miles upstream. We can assume that conglomerate eroded from the Bofecillos and Chisos Mountains filled the present Rio Grande valley between Lajitas and Boquillas Canyon at least up to these levels 2½ million years ago. Only the high peaks of the Chisos, Dead Horse and Bofecillos Mountains would have protruded above the conglomerate. The Rio Grande joined the Rio Conchos at Presidio about 2¼ million years ago (see page 32) and may have helped accelerate erosion.

The valley was emptied of conglomerate at the rate the river could cut down through the hard limestone barriers of the Mesa de Anguila, Mariscal Mountain and the Dead Horse-Sierra del Carmen range. The canyons created in the barriers, the Santa Elena, Mariscal and Boquillas Canyons are all today about 1,600 feet deep, an impressive feat and if done at an even rate over the 2 ½ million years, equivalent to just under three-quarters of an inch per hundred years.

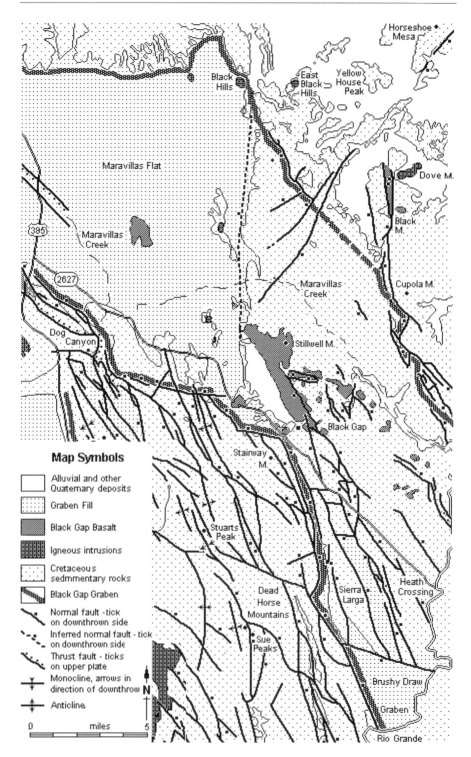

Geology: Persimmon Gap to Heath Crossing along FM 2627

FM 2627 Persimmon Gap – Heath Crossing

28 Miles

FM 2627 is one of the least traveled hardtop roads in Brewster County but one of the most interesting scenically and geologically. It follows the Black Gap Graben from Maravillas Flat east of Persimmon Gap to the Rio Grande, 1,200 feet below. Halfway down, it goes through a narrow canyon between the dark basalt mountains of the Black Gap and the beautiful limestone cliffs of the Dead Horse Mountains. Its final 10 miles follows Heath Canyon down to the river through open country with fine views across to the heights on both sides of the graben. The sharp pointed peak of Pico Etereo and the other mountains of northern Coahuila in Mexico are on the skyline in front most of the way. Food and cold drinks are available year round at the Stillwell store, 6 miles south and at the Open Sky Café on the Rio Grande, open all year except in the height of summer.

Mileages are measured from the junction of Fm 2627 and Highway 385. Strata down by the river are described in the table on pages 76-77.

Black Gap Graben

FM 2627 branches off Highway 385 about a mile north of Persimmon Gap. It is well worth the time to stop at the parking area at the junction to view the stunning panorama to the north and east. Taking FM 2627 as 12 o'clock, the view from 6:00 to 11:00 o'clock is across Maravillas Flat, a very level expanse of gravel-filled terrain in the Black Gap Graben, to distant escarpments and mesas.

The graben is the most easterly Basin and Range graben in the Big Bend, about 3,000 feet deep near the Rio Grande. It shallows and dies out towards the Maravillas Escarpment although it may continue a few miles north in the Santiago Flats to the left of Highway 385 as shown on the geological map on page 54. Its other boundaries are shown on the map opposite. A series of igneous plugs have been intruded along the northern boundary of the graben, including Sosa Peak at 7 o'clock and an unnamed one 3 miles east. Three others can be seen about 9 o'clock, an unnamed small plug, the double intrusion of Black Hills to its right, and then East Black Hills. Maravillas Flat is underlain by gravel. The eastern boundary of this gravel is the fault shown as a broken line on the map on page 100. The fault drops strata 1,600 feet down into the graben near Stillwell Mountain. Maravillas Creek has created a canyon 320 feet deep where it crosses this fault, the amount of movement on the fault since the creek began flowing. Several intrusions are found along or near the fault. One of them, two miles south of the Black Hills, contains fragments of rock brought up from the earth's mantle, 20 or more miles below.

Horseshoe Mesa is on the distant skyline, 23 miles away at 9:30 o'clock. The mesa is a fault block standing 1,260 feet above its base, its shape a horseshoe opening to the west. The small butte next to it, Yellow House Peak (3,250 feet), 450 feet above the plain, is part of the same block. Other mesas beyond Horseshoe Mesa are at the southeast corner of the Marathon Basin.

At 10 o'clock, to the right of Horseshoe Mesa, Dove Mountain (3,792 feet) is an intrusion resembling a packsaddle, 18 miles to the east-northeast (photograph on page 88). To its right, Black Gap Basalt, preserved in a down-faulted block, caps the dark butte of Black Mountain (3,642 feet). Both hills rise about 1,000 feet above their surroundings. Cupola Mountain (3,988 feet), an anticline in Santa Elena Limestone, is the large whale-backed mountain at 11 o'clock. The dark basalt remnant on its peak looks just like a cupola. One of the faults on the Black Gap Graben boundary has created a fault scarp 1,300 feet high facing the road at 11:30 between Cupola Mountain and Stillwell Mountain to its right. Stillwell Mountain is made up of a basalt flow down folded into a syncline. At 12 o'clock on the skyline the very sharp Pico Etereo is a rhyolite intrusion 35 miles to the southwest in Mexico.

Upper Cretaceous strata are preserved in the graben and crop out in roadcuts. Very distinctive creamy-colored flaggy Boquillas limestones crop out intermittently along the entire route. Ten miles south of Highway 385, the road goes through banks of weathered khaki-colored Pen Formation mudstone on a ridge. Patches of gravel graben fill crop out in road cuts and in mounds, in some places quite strongly stratified and pink-tinged at times.

The Black Gap Wildlife Management Area

The Black Gap Wildlife Management Area (WMA) takes its name from a pass in a dark basalt ridge east of the road about 17 miles south of Highway 385. The Texas Game and Wildlife Department operates and manages 52 wildlife management areas used for habitat conservation, wildlife research, demonstrations, and a variety of outdoor recreational activities. The Black Gap WMA at 107,000 acres is the second largest, an L-shaped area that FM 2627 enters 7 miles south of Highway 385. It runs parallel to the road to the Rio Grande and then follows the river downstream for 20 miles. The principal game species are desert mule deer, javelina, dove, rabbit, and scaled (blue) quail. Bobcat and coyote are also found. Regulations about hunting and camping in the WMA can be found in the Internet site *www.tpwd.state.tx.us/wma/wmarea/black_gap.htm*. The WMA has provided a series of numbered parking areas, which make convenient reference points for describing the scenery.

The Dead Horse Mountains

For the first five miles or so from Highway 385, the road runs along the narrow Laramide-age monocline of the Santiago Mountains. Two miles south, Persimmon Peak (3,749 feet) is on the west skyline on the upthrown side of the Black Gap Graben boundary fault. On the downthrown side of the fault, thick beds of Santa Elena limestone crop out along the road in low hills for the next several miles, dipping slightly to the south and to the west (photograph on page 88). They are faulted parallel to the road to form a series of cuestas in which their fault scarps face the road.

About four miles south of Highway 385, the cleft of Dog Canyon appears briefly in the escarpment on the left, a narrow gorge cut 800 feet deep through the mountains by Nine Point Draw. South of the canyon, the range broadens out into the Dead Horse Mountains, also called the Sierra del Carmen on maps. They rise in light gray limestone crags above the road, jagged and serrated compared to the Santiago Mountains. Along FM 2627 fault blocks form elongated diamond-shaped mountains delimited by Laramide-age faults running north-northwest and west-northwest, and separated by pull-apart grabens formed during Basin and Range extension. Most are tilted to the southwest and have been eroded down to the main ridge-forming formation in the area, the Santa Elena Limestone. Faults and grabens have been opened out into narrow valleys between the blocks; the landscape follows the geological structures very closely.

The first diamond-shaped mountain at roadside begins at 12 miles south of Highway 385, where its prow, almost like an upside-down boat, is at 3 o'clock from a WMA road. It is a horst of Santa Elena Limestone, flanked by faults on east and west. The Black Gap Graben boundary skirts its nose and runs west to about Dog Canyon before turning north along the Santiago Mountains.

A mile ahead, Bear Creek flows through a water gap at 3 o'clock, following a northeast-southwest fault cutting across the block with a downthrow to the north.

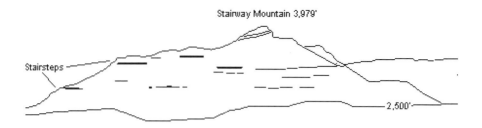

Stairway Mountain from 13.3 miles south on FM 2627

Stairway Mountain (3,979 feet) is the second prominent fault block along FM 2627, its nose on the right about 17 miles south of Highway 385. The mountain takes its name from the way Santa Elena and Sue Peaks limestone beds have eroded to create a very distinctive stairstep-like profile, 1,525 feet high. The Black Gap Graben boundary fault runs along its base near the road. Displacement on the fault is about 2,000 feet down towards the road here (photograph on page 89).

Black Gap Basalt

The first up-close view of the Black Gap Basalt is at ten miles down FM 2627 where the massive bulk of Stillwell Mountain (3,658 feet) looms 1,000 feet over the road in front (photograph on page 88). The mountain was named for Roy Stillwell, a pioneer cattleman who began ranching in the area in 1906, and whose family own the Stillwell RV park, store and ranch about six miles south on FM 2627. The basalt is about 22 million years old, 30 million years younger than the Dead Horse Mountains. Small plugs and dikes of basalt are widespread around Stillwell Mountain, the remains of vents and fissures through which the lava erupted. The lava is found as far north as Dove Mountain and as far west as Maravillas Flat. It consists of several flows separated by vesicular zones, and has a maximum thickness of 450 feet on the east side of Stillwell Mountain. (Vesicles are cavities formed by bubbles trapped in the lava as it solidifies).

The basalt is at roadside at the WMA headquarters, dark and rough (photograph on page 89). Just beyond the headquarters entrance, the road enters a canyon with low lava-capped hills on both sides of the canyon. Once out of the canyon, 2 miles ahead, the southern end of Stillwell Mountain on the left is a quite level ridge capped by a thick lava bed. Three more lava beds crop out on its flank.

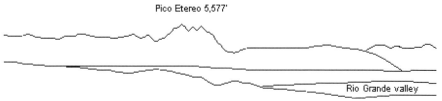

Pico Etereo from Parking Area 4

Heath Canyon

At Parking Area 4, 20 miles south of Highway 385, Heath Canyon, named for the English pioneer settler Tom Heath, broadens out into an open valley running down to the river. The stunning 180-degree panorama begins with the Santa Elena Limestone mesas on the skyline at 9 o'clock, 1,400 feet above the road on the far side of the Black Gap Graben. The sharp multiple-crested peak at 12 o'clock is Pico Etereo (5,577 feet), a rhyolite intrusion on the eastern edge of the Sierra del Carmen, the continuation of the Dead Horse range across the Rio Grande (photograph on page 90). The Dead Horse Mountains on the right are at their most spectacular as a series of notched crests on a continuous ridge, a monocline facing west. Stuarts Peak (5,107 feet) is at about 3 o'clock, 2,500 feet above the road. Two miles south, the twin summits of the Sue Peaks (5,854 and 5,845 feet) are the highest points in the range, 3,300 feet above FM 2627.

At 3 o'clock, the northern end of Sierra Larga (3,150 feet), a fault block within the Black Gap Graben, is tilted to the west and the south with thick Santa Elena Limestone beds cropping out in its face. Behind and parallel to it is the continuation of the Stairway Mountain ridge, 1,000 feet higher. Brushy Draw Graben separates the two, a narrow canyon floored with Boquillas limestone for 8 miles and then opening into a wide alluvium-covered flat near the river.

At Parking Area 5, the road winds down through low eroded hills of gravelly graben fill. Schott Tower (7,022 feet) is the high point in the Mexican Sierra del Carmen at 2 o'clock. Two miles ahead, the road goes through a saddle where thinly bedded Boquillas limestone crops out in roadcuts.

Just beyond the saddle, Parking Area 7 is good place to view the mountains to the west. The gravel road on the right goes down a graben between Sierra Larga and an unnamed horst on its left to Brushy Draw Graben and Stillwell Crossing on the Rio Grande. Brushy Draw Graben is a sub-graben of the Black Gap Graben. Two bare limestone noses, of a spur to Sierra Larga and of the unnamed horst, face the parking area.

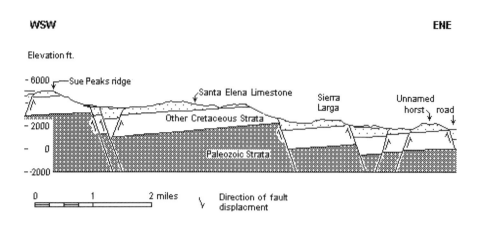

Section across the Dead Horse Mountains from FM 2627 to Sue Peaks ridge

A mile ahead, the road winds along between gravel banks, poorly bedded Buda limestone and thinly bedded Boquillas limestone exposed in roadcuts. The beautifully sculpted, sheer rock faces on the Dead Horse Mountains at 3 o'clock are spectacular (photograph on page 90).

At Parking Area 8 and for the next half-mile, the road cuts through stratified gravel, remnants of the material that had filled the graben at one time. Bedded Boquillas limestones crop out below in the Heath Canyon watercourse for the next mile or so. On the right the unnamed ridge has two Santa Elena Limestone beds exposed in its face.

The cross section above begins about a half-mile beyond Parking Area 8 and crosses the Dead Horse Mountains at approximately right angles to the faulting. It intersects the Sue Peaks ridge midway between Stuarts Peak and Sue Peaks. The road is on a down-dropped block of Santa Elena strata at the right of the section. Immediately to its left, strata are faulted up 800 feet to create the unnamed horst. After two minor faults, strata are further faulted up 900 feet on to Sierra Larga. Beyond the graben to the left of Sierra Larga, a major fault raises strata another 2,000 feet. Finally, a fault to the right of Sue Peaks ridge raises strata another 1,300 feet. Beyond the Sue Peaks ridge, successive faults and a monocline bring the strata down into the National Park at Tornillo Flat. Note how the strata dip to the right at about 5 degrees, so that although the cumulative displacement on all the faults combined is 5,000 feet, the Sue Peaks ridge, 5,400 feet elevation, is only 3,240 feet above the road.

One mile ahead, a Santa Elena Limestone fault block runs obliquely across the road from the right, an offshoot of the ridge the road has followed for the last 2 miles. It dips to the north at about 7 degrees. Fresh Santa Elena surfaces are pinkish cream in color.

Beginning at Parking Area 9, the road descends through thick limestone beds of the fault block. A half-mile ahead, it crosses a dry streambed over a concrete bottom where thinly bedded Buda limestone outcrops under gravels at the roadside. Further ahead, gravel banks and ridges of graben fill border the road for the next mile.

Heath Crossing

At Parking Area 10, 27.7 miles down FM 2627, the Rio Grande flows through the very narrow Irwin's Canyon at 9 o'clock. Upstream, the river sinuously winds along on the left to Heath Crossing. This crossing is one of the favorite put-ins for boating or rafting on the Rio Grande. The next access point, Dryden Crossing, is 85 miles downstream. The U.S. Congress in 1978 designated 196 miles of the Rio Grande, from the Coahuila-Chihuahua boundary in Mexico to the Terrell-Val Verde county line in the United States, as part of the National Wild and Scenic River System. Sixty of its miles are through remote canyons, the Lower Canyons of the Rio Grande, typically a 6- or 7-day trip, depending on the water level.

The Gerstacker Bridge at the road end 28 miles down FM 2627 is closed at the time of writing. It was built in 1964 to connect the fluorspar mining operations of Dow Chemical in Mexico with the railhead at Marathon, Mr. Gerstacker being a Dow Chemical director at the time. Fluorspar, the ore of fluorine, is found widely in Coahuila and Chihuahua, including around Pico Etereo. It occurs along contacts between limestone and igneous intrusions. Dow also built the hamlet of La Linda, across the river in Mexico, to house its employees. To its left, you can see the green processing plant where the fluorspar ore was crushed and concentrated before being trucked to the railhead. Du Pont bought Dow's mining operations and the bridge in 1971 but abandoned operations 20 years ago and donated the bridge to the National Parks and Conservation Association, a non-profit organization. The mines in Coahuila still operate but now supply only the Mexican market. There is talk of reopening the bridge for visitors to the Maderas del Carmen, a 545,000-acre nature protected area across the river from Big Bend National Park. A public telephone is at the U.S. end of the bridge.

Heath Canyon Ranch Inn is a quarter-mile away on the right. The 622-acre ranch, established in 1879, has 4000 feet of Rio Grande frontage where you can launch boats. Accommodation is available in a 3-bedroom unit with kitchen and in a bunkroom. RV parking is also available. The Open Sky Café is open except in the summer months.

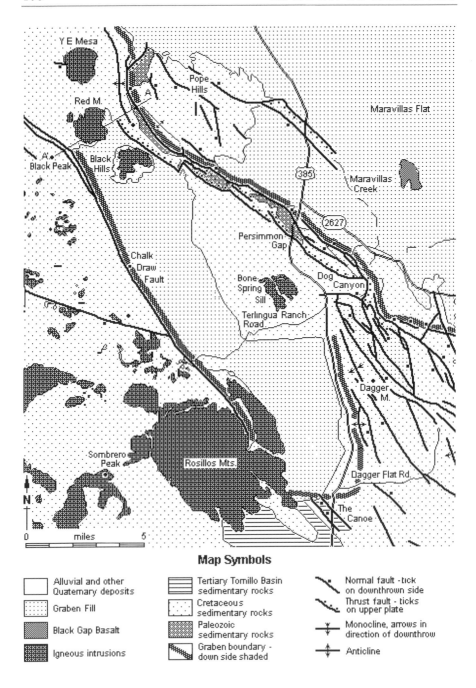

Map Symbols

Alluvial and other Quatemary deposits	
Graben Fill	
Black Gap Basalt	
Igneous intrusions	

Tertiary Tornillo Basin sedimentary rocks	
Cretaceous sedimentary rocks	
Paleozoic sedimentary rocks	
Graben boundary - down side shaded	

Normal fault - tick on downthrown side	
Thrust fault - ticks on upper plate	
Monocline, arrows in direction of downthrow	
Anticline	

Geology: Persimmon Gap to Dagger Flat

Persimmon Gap – Panther Junction

28 Miles

The Persimmon Gap – Panther Junction road begins at the entrance to Big Bend National Park and ends at the Park Headquarters. It offers the driver a great number of panoramas along the way beginning at the entrance to the Park where, looking back down Highway 385, Maravillas Flat is beautifully framed by mountains on all sides. Once in the Park, the road crosses through the Santiago Mountains at Persimmon Gap and passes into a series of low-lying grabens lying between the splendid Santiago and Dead Horse Mountains on the left and the many intrusions on the right. For the final 6 miles, the road runs on an alluvial pediment up to the Big Bend National Park headquarters at Panther Junction below the spectacular Pine Canyon caldera rim.

Mileposts are numbered from Panther Junction. Strata down by the river are described in the table on pages 76-77.

Persimmon Gap

Persimmon Gap (2,970 feet), named for the persimmon trees that used to grow there, is a mile uphill from Big Bend National Park entrance on the eastern side of the park. The pass is a wind gap, a low depression or notch in the mountains, 600 feet below the heights to right and left and 200 feet above the flats on either side. Calamity Creek runs parallel the Santiago Mountains on the west and perhaps it created the Gap at an earlier stage in the erosion of the northern park. Now it drains through Dog Canyon, 5 miles south and 400 feet lower.

Coming up to the summit, the spectacular cliff on the right has Glen Rose limestones about 300 feet thick at top with red sandstone and conglomerate, 30 feet thick, at its base. Underlying the Glen Rose strata, dark Tesnus shale and sandstone are exposed near the road on the right.

The Persimmon Peak cross-section on the next page illustrates the complex structure of the Santiago Mountains. Conglomerate and coarse sandstone of the Glen Rose Formation at the base of the Cretaceous are

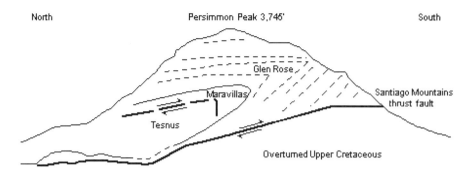

Section across Persimmon Peak

wrapped round an overturned anticline on the left. Within the anticline, a thrust fault has itself been folded, resulting in Maravillas strata lying over younger Tesnus strata. At the base of the peak, Glen Rose sedimentary rocks are separated from overturned upper Cretaceous strata by the main Santiago Mountains thrust fault, which runs from Red Mountain to Dog Canyon (photograph on page 91).

The Rosillos Mountains dominate the skyline at 1 o'clock from Persimmon Gap Ranch road below the visitor center. The very jagged Chisos Mountains appear on their left flank. Paisano Peak (5,400 feet) and East Corazon Peak (5,319 feet) are the two sharp intrusions at 2 o'clock, about 20 miles away north of the Park. The flat-topped Nine Point Mesa (5,480 feet) is at 3 o'clock. Black Peak (4,791 feet), another intrusion, is at 4:30 o'clock, 15 miles away.

Chalk Draw Graben

The Chalk Draw Graben is in the immediate foreground to the right, a broad plain with occasional low hills, 22 miles long and about 5 miles wide. It dies away to the north around Red Mountain and to the south at Dagger Flat Auto Trail. The western boundary is the Chalk Draw Fault, whose scarp, from 400 to 500 feet high, you can see between Black Peak and the Rosillos Mountains. Displacement into the graben on this fault is 1,500 feet at Red Mountain, as shown in the cross-section opposite. The graben's eastern boundary is a monocline in the Santiago Mountains in which strata are down warped 4,000 feet. From Red Mountain to Dog Canyon, the monocline is replaced by a series of thrust faults, such as the Santiago Mountains thrust fault seen at Persimmon Gap. At Dagger Mountain, south of Dog Canyon where monoclines and normal faults form the graben boundary, the downthrow is 1,700 feet (see page 113).

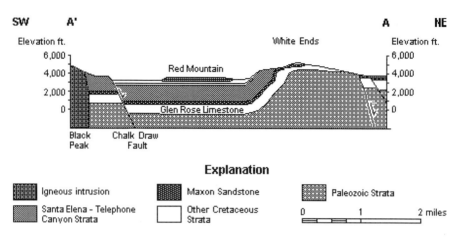

Section A – A': Chalk Draw graben from White Ends to Black Peak (see page 108)

Before Dog Canyon developed and provided an exit route for eroded sedimentary rocks, the graben fill would have been 1,500 feet thick and the uplands to its west would have had a cover of Pen and Aguja strata. These rocks have all been carried out through Dog Canyon, the lowest point in the graben, and only a thin veneer of basin fill remains, through which scattered Aguja outcrops appear. The basin fill is best preserved from Dog Canyon to the graben's southern boundary. It is thin elsewhere and is largely absent at roadside from Persimmon Gap to Dog Canyon.

Two miles south of Persimmon Gap on the right, flat-topped mesas and small hills of an eroded basalt sill stand up above the Aguja sandstone into which it was intruded. Basalt resists erosion better than the sandstone but despite that, Bone Spring Draw has cut a valley 100 feet deep through the middle of the sill. The creek, in a wetter period, must have been set in its course before the graben was eroded down to the top of the sill, and once established in its channel, was not deflected by the harder sill.

Dog Canyon

The diagram on page 112 is drawn from a photograph taken at the Dog Canyon Exhibit on the left. Several branches of the main Santiago Mountains thrust fault are exposed in the walls of the canyon in as complicated a structure as that seen at Persimmon Peak. Paleozoic override Cretaceous strata, Lower Cretaceous override Upper Cretaceous strata, and so on. However, thrust faulting ends just south of Dog Canyon. There are no thrust faults in the Dead Horse range.

Thrust faults can be seen in the escarpments on both sides of Dog Canyon

Dog Canyon separates the Santiago Mountains the Dead Horse Mountains, which on this side of the range, consist of a series of monoclines along its crest and western flanks. The floor of the canyon (2,560 feet) is the lowest point in the northern Park, over 400 feet below Persimmon Gap. Sands and gravels carried by Nine Point Draw began cutting through the mountains when the ground surface in Chalk Draw Graben was 900 feet higher than it is now, and continued until today's canyon floor level was reached. Of course, the area must have had higher rainfall than at present.

Nine Point Draw has a substantial creek bed, 40 to 50 feet wide and 10 feet deep, where it crosses the road 2 miles ahead. It rises near Nine Point Mesa, 30 miles to the west, and runs east until captured by Maravillas Creek, which runs south to the Rio Grande. Early drainage off the volcanic hills ran east towards the Pecos River before the Rio Grande developed, and Nine Point Draw and its upstream source, Calamity Creek, was one of the main outlets for carrying eroded debris out of the northern Park.

At 9 o'clock from Mile 23, a landslide has created a scar in the cliff and sent huge boulders down to the base of the escarpment. Although the scar looks quite new, it was actually created in 1987. Soft Del Rio claystones under the thrust fault eroded, undercutting the overlying Santa Elena limestone until it collapsed. You can see older scars every now and then along the cliffs if you look carefully.

Terlingua Ranch Road on the right leads to Terlingua Ranch Resort 23 miles away and to Highway 118, 33 miles west. It is a well-maintained county gravel road, open to the public and providing excellent views over the northern park and the Christmas Mountains.

The first monocline in the Dead Horse Mountains is at Dagger Mountain, two miles beyond Terlingua Ranch Road, where the limestone cliffs of the whale-shaped mountain stand up above the road on the left. The hill is named for the giant dagger yuccas that grow on its flanks. The best view of the monocline is from Dagger Flat Auto Trail, 5 miles ahead.

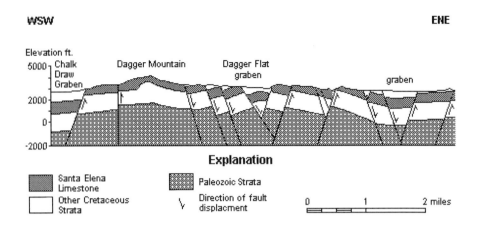

Section across Dagger Mountain, Dagger Flat and the Dead Horse Mountains

The Rosillos Mountains

Several intrusive sills in the Cretaceous rocks around and to the south of Dagger Mountain create low hills with gullies between them. On the right, it is quite level across the graben to the Rosillos Mountains foothills. The Rosillos dominate the skyline at 3 o'clock, roughly circular, seven miles across, massive and rounded, made up of a set of quartz trachyte sills probably laccolithic in part. The flat base of the intrusion is exposed by the Chalk Draw Fault, which runs into the intrusion and separates the main mountain mass from the ridge nearer the road (photograph on page 91). Rosillos Peak (5,445 feet) is the highest point in the mountains, 2,500 feet above the road.

Dagger Flat

Turn left on the Dagger Flat Auto Trail at Mile 13 to see the giant yuccas or daggers and to cross to the base of the Dead Horse Mountains. It is a well-maintained gravel road 7 miles long. Dagger Mountain on the left is a folded arch of Santa Elena limestone, part of a heavily faulted monocline facing west. The section above is across the Dagger Mountain summit at right angles to the folding and faulting about 5 miles north of the auto trail. Normal faults downthrow strata on either side of the mountain, about 1,500 feet into the Chalk Draw graben on the left, 1,700 feet into the Dagger Flat graben on the right. On the right of Dagger Flat graben is an anticline and a graben.

As you drive past Dagger Mountain, a basalt sill shows up as a black band near the top of dark gray Boquillas limestones at 10:30 o'clock.

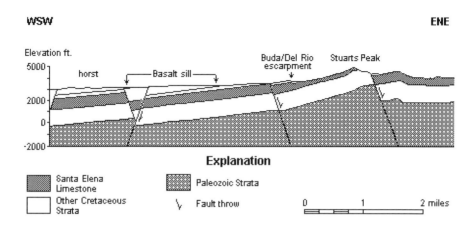

Section across the Dead Horse Mountains from Stuarts Peak west

Straight-ahead, the nearly flat-topped Dead Horse Mountains are cut every now and then by V-shaped notches. The ridge in front is Stuarts Peak (5,107 feet), seven miles long. South of it, the Sue Peaks (5,854 and 5,845 feet) are the highest summits in the range. All three peaks are on the crest of the major monocline in the mountains. The section above crosses the monocline a half-mile south of the Stuarts Peak summit. Faulting is much less intense than at Dagger Mountain but otherwise the structure is similar. On the left, a horst similar to Dagger Mountain is bounded by a fault on its left that drops strata 1,800 feet into the Tornillo graben, and on its right by a 1,000-foot fault that creates a graben similar to the Dagger Flat graben. From there, strata rise gradually to the crest above. Notice how the Santa Elena beds dip down from the summit roughly parallel to the slope. As a consequence, you see very few bedding planes along the escarpment for the next several miles.

Three miles from the Persimmon Gap – Panther Junction road, the trail enters a valley cut in Boquillas limestone where giant daggers grow in profusion. The road then turns to the left and follows a narrow valley between a cuesta escarpment capped by Buda Limestone on the left (the Buda/Del Rio escarpment on the cross section above) and the Dead Horse foothills on the right.

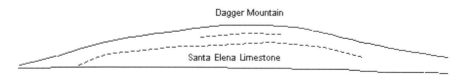

Dagger Mountain from Mile 13.5

The Tornillo Basin

Returning to the Persimmon Gap – Panther Junction road, Slickrock Mountain is the very sharp craggy peak looking like a stairstep at 2 o'clock. Croton Peak at 2:30 o'clock resembles a cuesta with an escarpment on its right. The southern boundary of the Chalk Draw Graben is at Mile 13 just beyond the Dagger Flat Auto Trail intersection. For the next two miles buff-colored Aguja sandstones, siltstones and mudstones crop out east of the road. These late-Cretaceous, non-marine sedimentary rocks were created in the Tornillo Basin by rivers in a swampy wet environment, very like today's bayou country in East Texas and South Louisiana. Fossilized dinosaur bones, turtles and logs, even logjams, have been found here.

Tertiary Sedimentary rocks

At Mile 11, the road crosses on to Tertiary sedimentary rocks at Tornillo Flat, a plain rimmed by badlands. These rocks provide some of the Park's most unusual scenery, a colorful flatland and badlands terrain with brightly-colored stream and flood plain rocks of purple, white, gray and tan.

Badlands most often develop in a semiarid climate where rains are heavy and there is little vegetation, and where rocks are made up of impervious claystone or shale alternating with layers of soft sandstone. They wear down into a maze of gullies; pinnacles erode into the fantastic shapes called hoodoos in the Southwest. Badlands occur in many places in the National Park in soft non-marine sedimentary rocks.

The flat-bottomed area rimmed on three sides by badlands at 2 o'clock from Mile 11 is called The Canoe, because of its shape. A small graben lies between two faults running northwest southeast about a half-mile apart, and within the graben, strata dip in to the center to create a canoe-like syncline. The graben is filled with sandstones and volcanic tuffs of the Canoe Formation, named after the location. The cockscomb-like crests of the Chisos Mountains dominate the horizon from 1 to 3 o'clock. Nugent Mountain is off to the left.

At Mile 9, purplish colored Black Peaks gravels crop out at 3 o'clock, overlain by Hannold Hill sandstones carved into a hoodoo (photograph on page 92). More Black Peaks sedimentary rocks crop out a half-mile ahead on the left, claystones and sandstones coated by dark, shiny desert varnish. Desert varnish is made up of iron oxide with traces of manganese oxide and silica. It is left by water evaporating from a rock's surface in a desert climate. The longer the rock is exposed to the atmosphere, the thicker the varnish becomes.

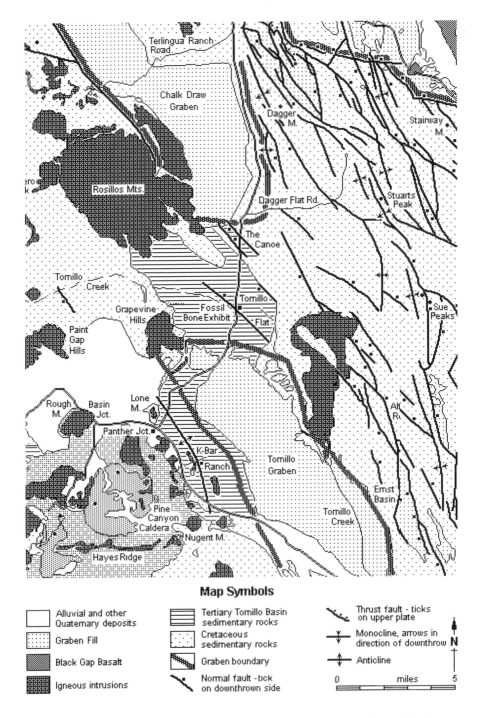

Map Symbols

Alluvial and other Quatemary deposits

Graben Fill

Black Gap Basalt

Igneous intrusions

Tertiary Tomillo Basin sedimentary rocks

Cretaceous sedimentary rocks

Graben boundary

Normal fault - tick on downthrown side

Thrust fault - ticks on upper plate

Monocline, arrows in direction of downthrow

Anticline

0   miles   5

N

Geology: Dagger Flat to Panther Junction along the Persimmon Gap – Panther Junction road

Cretaceous Javelina claystones crop out in the distance on both sides of the road, but are best seen on the right. They display a variety of color patterns ranging from green to buff to purple. Iron-rich minerals weather to shades of yellow and orange, and manganese-rich minerals to purple and black. The strata tilt or dip to the southwest at about 12 degrees.

Hannold Hill sedimentary rocks, greenish-gray with some purple hues, are exposed on the left near the Fossil Bone Exhibit at Mile 8.3. They dip to the south. The overlook above the exhibit has a display explaining the area geology. Finely bedded Hannold Hill sandstones and pebbly sandstones crop out in the immediate vicinity of the exhibit. The two Sue Peaks (5,854 and 5,845 feet) rise 3,100 feet above the overlook to the east, the highest points in the Dead Horse Mountains. Two of the Black Peaks can be seen on the banks of Tornillo Creek about 3 miles east of the road. The Corazones Peaks beautifully frame the Christmas Mountains on the west horizon.

The Tertiary sedimentary rocks from Black Peaks to lower Canoe strata, particularly those in Tornillo Flat, have been a prolific source of mammalian fossils. The Fossil Bone Exhibit has replicas of bones found in the area including *Phenacotus*, a sheep-sized plant eater, one of the earliest hoofed animals, *Coryphoton*, a hippo-like mammal about 9-feet long, a plant eater but with canine-like teeth and *Hyracatherium*, the earliest known ancestor of modern horse: this fox-sized animal was often called *Eohippos*, the dawn horse. Other common creatures of the Eocene swamps were crocodiles, turtles, and garfish, similar to those living today.

On the other side of the long bridge over Tornillo Creek, several purplish colored hoodoos and isolated buttes underlain by yellowish-gray Hannold Hill claystones and sandstones show up on the right and for the next mile (photograph on page 92). A half-mile past the bridge, an outlier of finely bedded Canoe Formation sandstone crops out beside the road (photograph on page 93). The Grapevine Hills are on the right, quite craggy, broken up in places on top, derived from an eroded igneous intrusion, probably a laccolith. The base of the intrusion is covered so we can't be sure whether it is a laccolith or not. Three faults runs north-northwest across the intrusion. The middle one has created a 300-foot deep canyon, which you can see from here.

The McKinney Hills at 9 to 10 o'clock are part of an irregularly shaped laccolith, six miles long and three miles wide, of reddish-brown fine-grained quartz trachyte. Roys Peak (3,945 feet) at 10 o'clock is the highest point, standing 1,350 feet above Tornillo Creek. There, the intrusion is 950 feet thick. McKinney Hills and McKinney Springs were named for the McKinney brothers who were pioneer ranchers in the area. A candelilla wax factory operated two miles south of the springs from 1913 to 1919. Its ruins can still be seen there.

The Chisos Mountains from Mile 8

Candelilla wax is obtained from a shrub named *Euphorbia cerifera* indigenous to northern Mexico and the Big Bend. The wax, which protects the plant against the environment and prevents excessive evaporation, is extracted by boiling the plant. The hard wax has extraordinary oil retention properties and improves the stability and texture of cosmetic and pharmaceutical products.

Another wax factory operated at Glenn Spring, just south of the Chisos Mountains, and undoubtedly, the wood used to fuel the boilers contributed to the general lack of trees in the eastern National Park.

The Chisos Mountains Pediment

About 2 miles beyond the Tornillo Creek bridge, the road climbs quite steeply through creamy Hannold Hill mudstones on to a Quaternary conglomerate at the Hannold Draw campsite. The conglomerate was originally an alluvial fan of sand, gravel and boulders eroded off the Chisos Mountains, part of a pediment that surrounded the mountains. Only patches of the conglomerate remain, standing up as ridges 50 to 80 feet above the surrounding alluvium (photograph on page 93). The road runs between these ridges for the next 2 miles, the one on the left set back nearly a mile.

The Dead Horse Mountains are on the skyline on the left, and behind them, the continuation of the range in Mexico where elevations rise to 8,200 feet. Nearer Panther Junction, Nugent Mountain with its precipitous east cliff face is very prominent at about 10 o'clock.

At Mile 3, remnants of an igneous sill cap create a craggy ridge at 3:30 o'clock. Pulliam Peak dominates the horizon at 12 o'clock. A mile from Panther Junction, Lone Mountain stands by itself on the left, 600 feet above the highway. A craggy jointed sill at its summit dips steeply to the right, along with the Aguja sandstone and mudstone beds into which it was injected. The prominent columnar jointing in the sill indicates that it cooled near the surface; the rubble below is from broken up columns. The mountain is on the western limb of an anticline whose axis crosses the road at Mile 1 and dies out near Nugent Mountain.

A quarter mile ahead, the dike on both sides of the road is part of a ring dike, a roughly circular structure created when the Pine Canyon volcano collapsed into a caldera. In places, evaporated water has left iron and manganese oxides as orange, brown and black stains on the surfaces of the rocks, desert varnish. Some stains appear as concentric bands of color, known as *liesegang* banding. On the right side of the road, the dike is jointed into columns.

At the junction, turn left for Rio Grande Village and Boquillas Canyon, turn right for Panther Junction Park Headquarters and the west side of the Park.

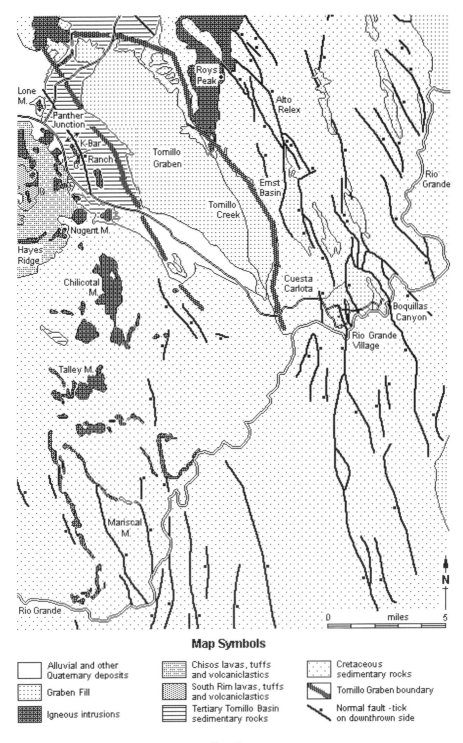

Geology: Panther Junction to Boquillas Canyon

Panther Junction – Boquillas Canyon

24 Miles

The Panther Junction – Boquillas Canyon road begins by rounding the Chisos Mountains on a pediment below the peaks of the Pine Canyon caldera. It then turns southeast and descends 1,800 feet into the Tornillo Creek graben, with the igneous intrusions of the southern Chisos Mountains on its right and the Tornillo Graben and the Dead Horse Mountains on its left. At the bridge over Tornillo Creek, it turns east and cuts through Cuesta Carlota, the most westerly fault block of the Dead Horse range, and enters the Rio Grande flood plain. There Rio Grande Village includes a visitor's center, campground, picnic sites, a store and service station. From Rio Grande Village, it crosses two small grabens in the Dead Horse Mountains along the river and ends at the entrance to Boquillas Canyon. Along the way, the route provides remarkable vistas across the Chisos Mountains to the South Rim, upstream along the river to Mariscal Mountain, across the river to the magnificent Sierra del Carmen escarpment in Mexico, and east to the low-lying Tornillo Creek valley and beyond it to western slopes of the Dead Horse Mountains. This is a remarkable 24 miles.

Mileposts are numbered from Panther Junction. Strata down by the river are described in the table on pages 76-77.

Turn right from the Park Headquarters parking lot on to the Rio Grande Village road. On the right above the road for the first three-quarters of a mile the light-colored dike of porphyritic rhyolite is part of a discontinuous ring dike around the Pine Canyon caldera, discussed in the Basin Junction – Chisos Basin section. On the crest of the hill at the K-Bar sign, stop and look over the Tornillo Creek valley below on the left. The road on the left leads to the old K-Bar Ranch headquarters, still standing, and a water well used by the Park Service. A porphyritic rhyolite sill tilted away from the road creates a ridge that hides the house from the road. It is on the west limb of an anticline running from Lone Mountain to Nugent Mountain. Alluvial gravels over Canoe Formation mudstones underlie the ground sloping down to the ridge. These mudstones crop out intermittently around intrusions and down by the Tornillo Graben until Mile 5.

The Dead Horse Mountains provide a beautiful backdrop on the left skyline. The western part of the range consists of a series of fault blocks crested by Laramide-age monoclines. The first of these blocks to come into view is Alto Relex (4,000 feet) on the right flank of Roys Peak at 9 o'clock. It is a horst uplifted between two faults, its crest a monocline in Santa Elena limestone. The fault scarp on this side of the block is 800 feet high; displacement on the fault is 1,600 feet down towards the road.

The Tornillo Graben

From about 4 to 6 o'clock, coarse conglomerates of the Estufa Canyon Formation create a line of low brown ridges. They are in the Tornillo Graben, a Basin and Range graben 16 miles long and 5 miles wide. The floor of the graben is estimated to have dropped 1,000 feet, all in the last 10 million years. The fault on its eastern boundary is hidden in alluvium; Tornillo Creek follows its approximate trace along the foothills of the Dead Horse Mountains. The northern boundary is obscured by pediment gravels but is probably somewhere in the vicinity of the bridge over Tornillo Creek, 8 miles north of Panther Junction. The southern boundary is covered by fan and pediment gravels; its position is uncertain. An escarpment in the alluvium runs from Dugout Wells to the Grapevine Hills, evidence of recent movement along an underlying fault, which is thought to be the western boundary of the graben. About 1,500 feet of Estufa Canyon alluvial fan deposits are exposed in the northeast part of the graben. At its base, two alluvial fans are up to 500 feet thick, the older of which is 9 million years old. They are made up deposits from streams that drained to the north, perhaps into an ancestral Pecos River. The upper 1000 feet is coarse gravel, of the same age as the Fingers Formation on the other side of the Chisos Mountains, 2 Ma at most.

The dry erosion channel at Mile 3 is the site of an old watercourse that has cut a water gap through the sill on the left of the road. Joined by two more runoff streams from the Chisos Mountains on the other side of the sill, it runs in the 100-foot deep Estufa Canyon through Estufa Canyon strata down to Tornillo Creek.

At Mile 4, the road starts down a pediment slope toward the Rio Grande. It runs on a lag gravel cap that covers most of the underlying graben fill for the next 10 miles. Lag gravel is made up of coarse, hard rock fragments that remain on a surface after the finer material has been blown away by wind. The gravel shows up in a number of low banks on either side of the road a quarter-mile ahead.

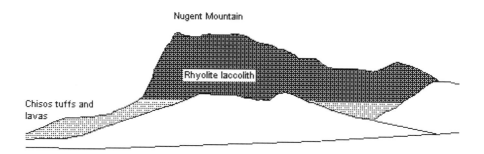

Nugent Mountain has one of the most distinctive profiles in the National Park. The base of the laccolith is approximate. This view is from the rise beyond the K-Bar Ranch road.

The Chisos and the Dead Horse Mountains

The Boquillas Canyon road provides excellent views of the Chisos Mountains from the southeast, as well as the other intrusions south of the main body. First on view is Nugent Mountain (4,783 feet), a rhyolite laccolith rising 1,400 feet above the road at Mile 4. At the northeast corner of its base, Chisos tuffs and lavas overlie Canoe Formation gray, purple, and mottled claystone, tuffaceous claystone, mudstone and siltstone and Javelina Formation claystone and sandstone containing dinosaur bones.

A mile ahead, the road to the right leads to Glenn Spring, the site of a candelilla wax factory and store. A party of Mexican bandits raided Glenn Spring on May 5, 1916, killing three U.S. soldiers and the storekeeper's son. A primitive road connects Glenn Spring to the River Road. At the Dugout Wells road, the South Rim (7,400 feet) comes into view, a platform jutting out from the main Chisos body, with an escarpment on its south side 2,250 feet high. It is capped by rhyolitic lava flows of the South Rim Formation, which is named after it. Hayes Ridge, a rocky uneven ridge up to 1,500 feet above the flats below, can be seen at 11 o'clock just west of Nugent Mountain. It is another segment of the ring dyke that we saw near Panther Junction. On the skyline behind Hayes Ridge, the jagged front of Crown Mountain (7,010 feet) is on the southern edge of the Pine Canyon caldera.

Dugout Wells, the site of springs marked by cottonwood trees, is on the left a mile beyond Glenn Spring road. The narrow battlement on the skyline at 12 o'clock is Schott Tower (7,022 feet), the high point in the Sierra del Carmen south of Boquillas Canyon. The Dead Horse Mountain range crosses into Mexico at Boquillas Canyon and extends southeast for 80 miles. On the Mexican side, it is never more than 10 miles wide and in

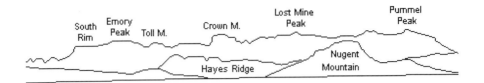

The full array of the Chisos Mountain are on display looking northwest from Mile 11.3, also seen in the photograph on page 94.

many places much less; the northern part consists of tilted fault blocks bounded by the southwest-facing escarpment now in view The first block over the river, the Sierra del Terminal, is about 1,250 feet high. The Sierra del Carmen escarpment behind it on its right flank is 3,600 feet high (photograph on page 94). The escarpment at nightfall is one of the most beautiful sights in the Park. Ross Maxwell described it well in his book *The Big Bend of the Rio Grande*: "The sunset on this cliff is a gorgeous sight, the like of which is seldom seen. In the afternoon when there are wispy clouds in the western sky, the sunlight strikes the rocks with an orange glow. As the sun sets, the colors brighten to a crimson hue. After the sun disappears, the colors fade for a brief period but are again brightened by the afterglow. Eventually, however, the colors change to pink, then bluish gray and purple. These colors may be seen long after the light has disappeared from the other mountains – then all colors eventually fade into the blackness of night".

A mile further on, Chilicotal Mountain (4,104 feet) at 3 o'clock is a thick rhyolite sill set in Javelina shales and sandstones. The sill crops out in a cliff at the summit and in a second cliff halfway down the mountain. Elephant Tusk (5,241 feet) on its right flank is a trachyte intrusion eroded into the shape of an elephant's tusk. At Tortuga Mountain (4,703 feet), just south of the South Rim at 4:30 o'clock, Aguja strata were domed, eroded, and intruded by a gabbro sill before deposition of the Chisos Formation. A later rhyolite stock, of similar composition to the Chisos Mountains pluton, holds up the 2-mile long dome today. *Tortuga* is Spanish for tortoise.

From the parking area just beyond Mile 9, Sierra San Vicente on the skyline at 1:30 is across the Rio Grande in Mexico. At 2:00 o'clock, Mariscal Mountain (3,932 feet) is on both sides of the Rio Grande, which has cut Mariscal Canyon through it, 1,800 feet deep. Both mountains are anticlines in a line of anticlines running north through the Chisos Basin to the Christmas Mountains, all created during the Laramide Orogeny. The Mariscal Mine, at the north end of Mariscal Mountain, produced about

1,300 flasks of mercury between 1900 and 1923 under a series of owners. At 3 o'clock, Black Knob is a spine-like trachyte intrusion.

Cuesta Carlota (3,018 feet) is the low dark brown ridge at 9 o'clock. It is the most westerly of the Dead Horse fault blocks, a cuesta of Buda and Del Rio strata, faulted on its eastern side. It runs south for 6 miles, crossing the road at Mile 18. The large number of erosion channels on the slope facing the road gives it an almost corrugated appearance.

The parking area on the right at Mile 13.5 is another good place to stop and look over the lower Park. A thick sill caps Talley Mountain (3,765 feet) at 3 o'clock, 22 miles to the southwest. The sills on Talley Mountain and Chilicotal Mountain may have been connected at one time. One of the best dinosaur bone beds found in the park is in an old quarry near Talley Mountain. Elephant Tusk is back in view, now on the right of Chilicotal Mountain.

The lag gravel cap that the road has been on since Mile 4 is discontinuous beyond this point. Erosion has cut through the gravels and exposed non-marine Aguja sandstone and claystone containing dinosaur bones, petrified wood, and some lignite. The skull and lower jaw of a 30-foot long crocodile, *Deinosuchus riograndensis,* weighing perhaps 2 tons, was collected near here. It is on display at the University of Texas at Austin. Another collected near Talley Mountain is on display at the Dallas Museum of Natural History. At 9 o'clock, Cuesta Carlota is cut by a water gap 400 feet deep through to the Ernst Basin graben on the other side of the ridge.

Tornillo Creek Bridge

At Mile 16, just before the bridge over lower Tornillo Creek, the road descends a steep hill and the River Road joins from the right. This road is quite passable by high clearance vehicles if not washed out by rains. Ask at the Park Headquarters about its condition before attempting to use it. If it is in good condition, it can be used to cross the southern Park to Ross Maxwell Scenic Drive near Castolon. It provides wonderful panoramic views of Sierra Vicente, Mariscal Mountain, the Chisos Mountains, Sierra Quemada, Punta de la Sierra, and across the Rio Grande into Mexico.

Dark khaki sandstone of the Aguja Formation crops out on both sides of the road at the junction with the River Road. Across the bridge, Pen Formation strata crop out on the left of the road, Boquillas on the right. An 18-inch thick dike crosses the road shortly beyond the bridge. The heat of the intrusion has baked rocks for 6 feet on either side of it.

For the eight miles between Tornillo Creek and its terminus at Boquillas Canyon, the road crosses through the west side of the Dead

Horse Mountains, providing the only easy access to the internal structure of the range. In the first 1½ miles the road travels over the Cuesta Carlota fault block through Boquillas, Buda, Del Rio and Santa Elena Limestone strata. The block is tilted at 5 to 8 degrees to the west.

Hot Springs

The Hot Springs road is on the right at Mile 17. Several hot springs are found in a quarter-mile stretch of the riverbank about a mile south of the turnoff. Their water temperature is 105 degrees Fahrenheit year-round. They have been in use for many centuries as evidenced by pictographs on the cliffs nearby, depressions in the rocks used as mortars, kitchen refuse areas and a primitive bath chiseled out of the rocks. J. O. Langford purchased the land and springs from the state in 1909 and built a store on the wagon road between San Vicente and Boquillas that became a popular border trading post. A limestone bathhouse was later built over the hot springs and cabins erected for overnight visitors and health seekers. The Langfords sold the property to the state of Texas in 1942, although the resort continued in operation until 1952. Langford's *A Homesteader's Story* is an entertaining account of life in the early Big Bend.

Hot springs are quite common along Basin and Range faults in the Big Bend. Faults provide channels for water to circulate underground and then resurface. Temperatures rise about one degree Fahrenheit for each 50 feet as you go towards the center of the earth; average surface water temperatures here are 79° F, so to be heated up to 105° F., the Hot Springs water must have descended underground at least 1,300 feet. Hot Springs is in line with the western boundary fault of the Tornillo Graben which probably accounts for their existence.

The Old Ore Road

The Old Ore Road is on the left at Mile 18, at the top of a ridge capped by Santa Elena Limestone. The road was used for hauling lead and silver ore by mule teams from mines in the Sierra del Carmen in Mexico to the railroad in Marathon. The five miles to La Noria campsite are in good condition. A high clearance vehicle is needed for the remaining 21 miles to the Dagger Flat Auto Trail.

Cuesta Carlota and the Rio Grande Village Graben

Just beyond the Old Ore Road junction, the road goes through a wind gap 250 feet deep in Cuesta Carlota and then a short tunnel through a fault block of slightly pinkish Santa Elena Limestone. Before the tunnel was constructed, the road used to go round a curve on the right called

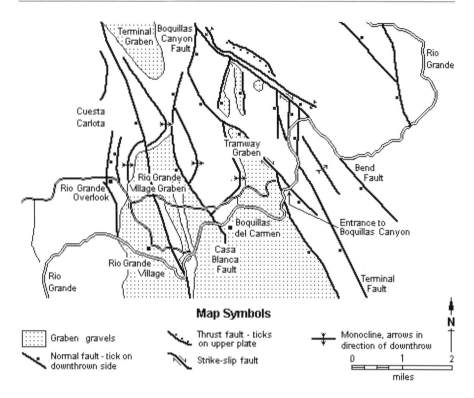

Structural sketch map of Boquillas Canyon area

Deadman's Curve, so called because Max Ernst, justice of the peace, storekeeper and postmaster at La Noria was fatally shot there in 1908. According to Martin Kohout, writing in the *Handbook of Texas Online,* the family of Martin Solis, who owned a competing store at Boquillas, was suspected, but no one was ever charged with the crime.

Once through the tunnel, the Rio Grande overlook at 3 o'clock provides a fine panoramic view over the Rio Grande Village graben to the village of Boquillas del Carmen in Mexico. The graben is about 2 miles wide and mostly underlain by gravels, as shown on the above map. It is a half graben, faulted down on only its western side by the Casa Blanca Fault. You can see the fault scarp at 12 o'clock. A monocline on its western boundary has a maximum displacement of 800 feet into the graben. Internal faults bring up two tilted fault blocks to the surface within the graben.

Rio Grande Village

At Mile 19 the road forks, one branch going to Rio Grande Village, the other to Boquillas Canyon. Rio Grande Village (1,850 feet) has a campground and a few scattered buildings, which include a visitor center, a United States Customs post, a store that sells gasoline and camping supplies, and a number of park employee residences. The store is open year-round; the visitor center is closed from April to November.

The fork on the right, the Boquillas Canyon road, continues across the graben round the northern end of the water tank fault block and across the second block, both referred to earlier. At Mile 20, the road descends the steep flank of the second block between cliffs as the foliage along the river comes into view. Boquillas del Carmen is at 1:30 o'clock in Mexico.

At 10:30 o'clock, Schott Tower (7,022 feet), the high point in the Sierra del Carmen escarpment, was named for Arthur Schott (1814-1875), naturalist, artist, engineer, poet, geologist, and musician. Beginning in late 1851, he worked for the United States Boundary Commission under Major W. H. Emory in surveying the boundary between Texas and its neighboring Mexican states. He collected botanical, geological, and zoological specimens, made notes on geology, plants, and animals and drew landscapes and Indians. The peak's name in Mexico is Cerro Pico Cerda and it is often called El Pico in the United States.

Barker Lodge, the large white house on the right used by the National Park Service for housing visiting research scientists, was built near the site of a settlement called Boquillas, which developed in 1883 when mining began in the Sierra del Carmen across the river. Kansas City Smelting and Refining Company, which became part of ASARCO in 1899, built a smelter in Boquillas and a cable tramway to carry ore across the river to the smelter from the mines.

A store opened in 1894 and a post office in 1896 when the local population was estimated as 300 on the Texas side of the river, including San Vicente, and 1,000 on the Mexican side. The smelter closed in 1911 and ore was then shipped by mule train to Marathon via the Old Ore Road and railed to the main ASARCO smelter in El Paso. In 1914, a group of Houston and San Antonio investors built a more elaborate cable tramway two miles downstream from the original tram. It terminated in the Ernst Basin about 3 miles north of Rio Grande Village. A road was built to connect the terminal to the Old Ore Road. This arrangement was successfully used until mining ended in the Sierra del Carmen in 1918.

Just beyond Barker Lodge, the road climbs 90 feet up the Casa Blanca Fault escarpment, and crosses a saddle in a Santa Elena Limestone block which is tilted to the east at 12 degrees. The road then descends a steep hill between limestone cliffs into the Tramway Graben. Like Rio Grande Village graben, it is a half graben in which a series of small faults and monoclines take strata down into the deepest part of the graben at the

Boquillas Canyon from the riverbank. The fault in the canyon wall is a branch of the Boquillas Fault. It has a downthrow of about 600 feet towards the viewer.

Boquillas Canyon Fault, its eastern boundary. This fault has displacement down to the southwest of at least 800 feet in the north of the graben and 600 feet in the Canyon.

Boquillas del Carmen is at 5 o'clock from Boquillas Canyon Overlook (photograph on page 95). The green structure is an old mill for crushing fluorite from mines at Sierra San Vicente, 15 miles southwest, and Sierra La Encantada, 50 miles south. Looking toward Boquillas Canyon at 11 o'clock, a fault block of Santa Elena Limestone is in the foreground. A second fault block can be seen behind it; the lowest strata are Del Carmen Limestone and the slope above is the Sue Peaks Formation, which is overlain by the Santa Elena Limestone. The Boquillas Canyon Fault is in front of the second block. Notice how all the blocks dip towards the river (photograph on page 95). The ore terminal trail is on the left just beyond the overlook road entrance. This 4-mile trail takes you up to the ore terminal at the north end of the aerial tramway built in 1914. The tramway itself passed overhead just beyond Mile 24. Old cable and pylons can still be seen near the road.

Boquillas Canyon

The Boquillas Canyon Parking Area is at Mile 24.3. The Boquillas Canyon Fault splits into three at this point. One is buried in the parking area alluvium; another is at the base of the escarpment on the left; the third is a quarter-mile down the canyon where Santa Elena Limestone in the cliff across the river is tilted to the northeast and faulted down 600 feet to the southwest. You can see this fault from the riverbank at the canyon entrance as sketched in the diagram above from the photograph on page 96. The map on page 127 shows the river turning north just beyond that fault. It follows a narrow graben between two north south trending faults. The blocks on either side of the river tilt towards it.

Further downstream, the Rio Grande turns southeast along the Bend Fault and then is deflected to the east along the front of a monocline. The river route through the Dead Horse Mountains thus follows the underlying structure and is not a matter of chance. The grabens are of Basin and Range age. They began forming about 25 Ma, 5 million years after the main volcanism ended, and created passageways for drainage off the volcanic highlands to the west. Once the river cut through the soft Upper Cretaceous rocks, it was trapped in its channel and continued cutting through the hard Lower Cretaceous strata. During the rainy season, summer and early autumn, the river carries many tons of sand and silt daily, the cutting tools used to create the canyon.

Boquillas Canyon is a favorite site for float trips down the river. The river is calmer here than in Santa Elena and Mariscal canyons, but the canyon is still an imposing sight. Its walls are mainly massive limestone, at most places rising 1,500 feet straight up from the water's edge. Many boulders have fallen from the walls creating some rapids but the canyon is navigable in a small boat or rubber raft. The canyon opens out at another graben at Stillwell Crossing 26 miles downstream. At Heath Crossing, a further 3 miles downstream, the river enters the lower canyons, a 135-mile section of the river through very scenic and remote country.

Panther Junction – Study Butte

25 Miles

The Panther Junction – Study Butte road takes the visitor across desert scenery between the splendid backdrops of the Chisos and Christmas Mountains. For its first 8 miles, it crosses a pediment sloping down from the base of the Chisos Mountains to Tornillo Creek. The pediment is cut in Chisos volcanic rocks left of the road and Cretaceous sedimentary rocks on the right. At Todd Hill, the road descends 250 feet to a younger pediment also cut in Cretaceous sedimentary rocks and follows it for a further 12 miles. Near the Park entrance, it drops a further 200 feet to the level of Terlingua Creek and its tributaries. It continues on that level to Study Butte through displays of vividly colored badlands. In the last 10 miles, there are wonderful vistas of the Christmas Mountains, 2,500 feet above the road to the right, and great numbers of smaller intrusions in their foothills.

Mileposts are numbered from Panther Junction. Strata in this area are described in the table on page 76-77.

Paint Gap

Turn left towards Study Butte on leaving the Park Headquarters parking lot. The peaks of Pine Canyon caldera are on the skyline at 9 o'clock. Lone Mountain is at 2:30 o'clock, a rhyolite sill overlying Aguja Formation sedimentary rocks dipping west on the flank of an anticline.

Peaks of the Pine Canyon caldera from the Park Headquarters parking lot

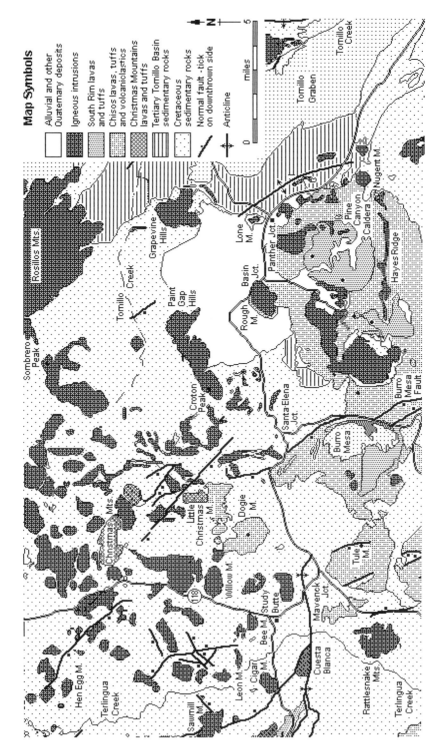

Geology: Panther Junction to Study Butte

The Grapevine Hills road junction is a good point to park and view the great panorama of igneous mountains from 3 to 10 o'clock on the skyline. At 4 o'clock, the Grapevine Hills are the remnants of an eroded rhyolite laccolith. At 3 o'clock, the immense Rosillos Mountains dome (5,445 feet) is on the skyline, an eroded and heavily faulted laccolith. Several of the faults have widened into canyons, some as much as 1,000 feet deep. One facing the road is about 600 feet deep. The round bald dome on its left, looking rather like the dome of a telescope observatory, is also part of the intrusion.

In front of the Rosillos Mountains, Tornillo Creek has carved a 300-foot deep valley across Javelina and Aguja mudstone and sandstone badlands, almost 1,000 feet below us. The valley is of recent vintage, having developed in the last 2 million years, but it reminds us that 60 million years ago, rivers and streams ran through the heavily forested Tornillo Basin at roughly the same elevation and direction and dinosaurs rumbled through the trees (photograph on page 96).

The Chisos Mountains pediment is made up of sands and gravels derived from the mountains and cemented by caliche. Caliche, mainly calcium carbonate, is deposited when water carrying dissolved calcium carbonate percolates up to ground surface and evaporates. It is widely used for road surfacing in West Texas.

The low ground at 12:30 o'clock is Paint Gap, the pass between the Chisos Mountains and the Paint Gap Hills. At 2:45 o'clock, immediately to the left of the Rosillos bald dome, the flat-topped Santiago Peak (6,521 feet) stands high above the general crest of the Santiago Mountains on the distant skyline, 35 miles away. Nine Point Mesa is the great slab on the skyline, 25 miles away, just to the right of Santiago Peak. Both are described in the Study Butte – Mitre Peak section of Chapter IV.

Immediately left of Nine Point Mesa, East Corazon Peak (5,045 feet) at 1:30 o'clock is part of a quartz trachyte intrusion. To its right, the steep-sided West Corazon Peak (5,319 feet) is a rhyolite intrusion. Both peaks rise some 1,500 feet in forbidding, near-vertical rock faces and broken inclines. *Corazon* is Spanish for heart. Supposedly a cleft in one of the peaks makes it resemble a heart.

Croton Peak is in the middle distance at 1 o'clock, a sharp intrusion standing up above Paint Gap. Behind it and to its right on the skyline, the Christmas Mountains (5,728 feet) are eroded from a faulted anticline pushed up by an intrusion.

For the next half-mile, the road crosses the eastern tip of the Government Spring laccolith, an intrusion of porphyritic trachyte into Chisos Formation strata. It crops out on Rough Mountain on the left ahead,

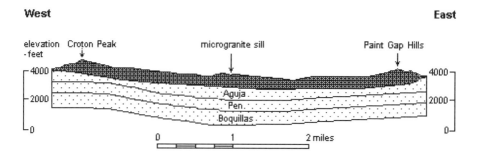

A continuous sill extends from the Paint Gap Hills to Croton Peak

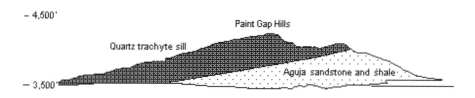

Paint Gap Hills from Grapevine Hills Road

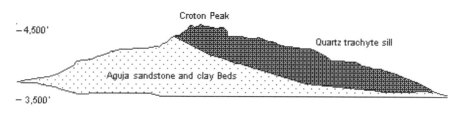

Croton Peak from Croton Springs road

500 feet above the road. The name comes from Government Spring across the road. The spring itself may have been named from the U.S. army camp set up there in the 1880s to protect the area from Apache and Comanche raiders.

The road turns southwest as it passes Paint Gap Road to go through Paint Gap. In the intermediate foreground, the long brown ridge from Croton Peak, the very craggy igneous mass at 2 o'clock, to the Paint Gap Hills (4,263 feet) at 4 o'clock, is a continuous quartz trachyte sill, as shown in the top cross section above and in detail in the lower two sections. It is tilted up at Paint Gap Hills to create a cuesta with a precipice to the east. The north side of Pulliam Peak is on the skyline at 9 o'clock.

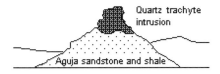

The Sphinx, an eroded remnant of a quartz trachyte intrusion in Aguja yellow sandstone and shale

Just after Mile 8, the road crosses the divide from the Tornillo Creek drainage basin to the Terlingua Creek basin, descending 250 feet down Todd Hill. It cuts through the Chisos Mountains pediment on the way down and exposes a remnant of a Pleistocene alluvial conglomerate fan. The main pediment in the Terlingua Creek basin is about 1,200 feet lower than the Chisos Mountains pediment, and very little of the latter remains there. The mountains of the basin are beautifully framed on the left. The Window is at 9 o'clock with Vernon Bailey Peak on its left, connected by a long northeasterly ridge to Pulliam Peak. Carter Peak and Ward Mountain are on its right.

The road cuts through Aguja strata at Mile 9 (photograph on page 193). A sill in the sandstone above the road at 10 o'clock creates high ground by its resistance to erosion. Several similar sills crop out in the next few miles.

The southwestern end of the Paint Gap-Croton Peak sill is on the right at Croton Peak Road. Rounding the end of a ridge capped by sill on the left, the small butte on the right is called the Sphinx for its fancied resemblance to the Egyptian monument. Some think it looks more like a camel or a bear.

Burro Mesa Fault

At Santa Elena Junction, turn left on to the Ross Maxwell Scenic Drive to see the southwest Park, Castolon and Santa Elena Canyon. The road is described in the Ross Maxwell Drive – Old Maverick Road section later in this chapter.

Burro Mesa (4,431 feet) in front is capped by Burro Mesa rhyolite and Wasp Spring flow breccia overlying Chisos tuffs, ash flows, and lavas. The Burro Mesa Fault, the boundary between the Chisos Mountains horst and the Castolon Graben, runs northwest along the base of the mesa and crosses the road at Mile 14. There, vertically dipping Aguja Formation beds dragged up by the fault crop out in the arroyo at 3 o'clock on the

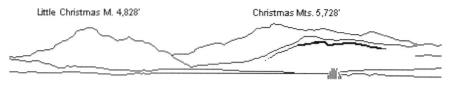

The view from Mile 11.8: the Chisos Pen anticline folds the trachyte sill in the ridge at front.

right; dark-colored Javelina claystone beds crop out on the left of the fault. Although displacement across the fault is down to the west, the mesa, on the downthrown side, stands 300 feet above the sandstones and claystones on the upthrown side, and more further south (see page 148).

Rounding Burro Mesa

The road turns north and runs parallel to the Burro Mesa Fault for about three-quarters of a mile. The Aguja ridge above the bend in the road on the right is the east limb of an anticline, the Chisos Pen anticline. Several trachyte sills have intruded it, making it resistant to erosion. The parking area at Mile 15 is a good point to view the anticline and the tall, spectacular peaks of Slickrock Mountain, West Corazone Peak, the Christmas Mountains and Little Christmas Mountain. Slickrock Mountain (3,986 feet) at 3 o'clock is a trachyte sill like that at Croton Peak and may be a remnant of the same sill. Its sharp crest and the 800-foot vertical cliff on its southwest side give it a dramatic cuesta-like profile. The crest of the Chisos Pen anticline runs north south through badlands between it and the road and has brought up older Pen and Boquillas strata to the surface. The Aguja sandstones on the ridge to the right dip away from the crest.

Rounding the corner ahead, the road descends 300 feet from the Burro Mesa volcanic strata on to a pediment of Javelina Formation mudstones and sandstones. The pediment is eroded on either side of the road by the valleys of Alamo Creek on the left and Rough Run Creek, a tributary of Terlingua Creek, on the right.

The panorama across Rough Creek from Mile 13.5

The Chisos Mountains and Burro Mesa from Mile 18

At 8:30 o'clock from Mile 16, a yellowish spine-shaped body, probably a volcanic neck can be seen in the center of a volcanic vent near the north end of Burro Mesa. The side facing the road has been eroded away. The vent is rimmed by lava on the other three sides. Further down Burro Mesa, quite some distance away, five lava flows crop out towards the right of the hill. An intrusive plug creates some low hills on the right of the road.

Little Christmas Mountain and the Christmas Mountains

Just beyond Mile 16, the dark Little Christmas Mountain (4,828 feet) is at 4 o'clock, its summit 1,750 feet above the draw to its right. The Christmas Mountains (5,728 feet) are on the skyline, a dome 5 miles long by 3 miles wide, capped by Cretaceous limestones and by the eroded remnants of several volcanic calderas. The dome is probably underlain by an unexposed intrusion that is responsible for the uplift, although an anticline may have developed during the Laramide Orogeny, creating some uplift prior to igneous activity. Such an anticline would align with the Chisos and Mariscal Mountain anticlines to the southeast.

Santa Elena Limestone strata dip off the summit to the right. The main volcanic calderas are on the northwest of the dome and near its center. Several massive sills in the limestone flank the dome, and volcanic breccia caps the highest peaks. The complex produced an extensive series of rhyolitic to quartz trachyte air-fall and ash-flow tuffs, silica-rich lavas and coarse debris-avalanche deposits.

Tuffs from the Christmas Mountains calderas were the source of volcaniclastic beds at Tule Mountain ahead and in the upper Canoe Formation at Tornillo Flat. Little Christmas Mountain is also built up of tuffs and lavas from this volcanic center. They sit on a platform of older Chisos Formation tuffs derived from volcanic ash originating in Mexico. Alamo Creek basalt crops out as a dark ledge at the base of the mountain. Many steep sided volcanic outliers have igneous vents at their cores, but that does not seem to be the case at Little Christmas Mountain.

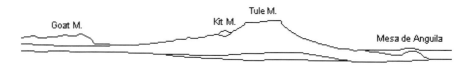

Tule Mountain from the Vertical Scenery Exhibit at Mile 20

At Mile 18, the low rough hill at 3 o'clock is Dogie Mountain (3,689 feet), rising 940 feet above the road. A volcanic outlier similar to Little Christmas Mountain, it is capped by ash-flow tuff and quartz trachyte lava from the Christmas Mountains overlying Chisos Formation strata. Its bare flanks look rather like those of Croton Peak. Note the jointing at the top and the wall of light gray Christmas Mountains tuff on its southwest flank. The ragged peaks to its north are of similar origin.

The Western Park

Tule Mountain (3,838 feet) is at 10 o'clock from the Vertical Scenery Exhibit at Mile 20. Kit Mountain is in the distance at 9 o'clock with the Mule Ear Peaks and Goat Mountain to its left. These peaks are described in the Ross Maxwell Drive – Maverick Road section. Mesa del Anguila is on the horizon in front, very level and even, from Tule Mountain to about 2 o'clock. Beyond it, on the skyline, are fine views of mountain ranges in Mexico. The nearest is Sierra del Mulato (5,427 feet), 10 miles west of Lajitas.

A half-mile beyond the exhibit, an anticline crosses the road running northwest towards Maverick Mountain. You can see it in the arroyo on the right. Pen Formation claystones have been folded up and are exposed on the eroded crest, with Aguja sandstone beds dipping away from the crest on both flanks.

Maverick Mountain (3,496 feet) stands 800 feet above the road at 3 o'clock, a small stock, 34 million years old, intruded into the preexisting anticline. It may have been a vent supplying volcanic lava to an earlier surface high above the present mountaintop. It stands alone, like a maverick steer, hence the name.

Old Maverick Road joins at Maverick Junction just beyond the Badlands Exhibit on the right. The varicolored claystones in the foreground are in the Javelina Formation. A fault crosses the road at the intersection and is in the creek bed at 3:00 o'clock, where Javelina strata on the left are dropped down into contact with Aguja strata on the right. At 9 o'clock, Tule Mountain rises 1,100 feet above the desert floor. Its upper stratum of Tule Mountain Trachyandesite, 200 feet thick, resembles the prow of a ship, tilted to the east. At the base of the mountain, light gray volcaniclastic beds crop out, ash-fall tuffs from calderas in the Christmas Mountains.

The road has been on a pediment for the last six miles, at about 2,750 feet elevation. Just beyond the intersection it descends through Javelina, Aguja and Pen Formation strata to the Dawson Creek valley 250 feet below.

The terrain underlain by Javelina strata is rough, badlands with colorful fossil soils, some purplish from manganese- or iron-rich minerals (photograph on page 193). Thin platy sandstone of the Aguja Formation is exposed in the arroyo of Dawson Creek. A quarter mile ahead, the road crosses on to Pen Formation yellow and gray claystone and sandstone strata (photograph on page 193).

On its way down into the Dawson Creek valley, the road cuts obliquely through the Terlingua monocline. Beds dip to the south across the monocline.

Terlingua Creek Valley

A 3-foot dike crosses the road just before the park exit at Mile 20 and the bridge over Dawson Creek. Badlands on the left expose variegated cream and pinkish brown Javelina claystones in an erosion escarpment facing the road. At 7:00 o'clock, the low black band is a sill in the Javelina Formation.

Rough Run Creek crosses the road a mile ahead. Just beyond, Study Butte (2,830 feet) rises 230 feet above the flats on the right. It was named for Will Study (pronounced "stoody") who around 1901 developed the Big Bend Quicksilver Mine on the left flank of the hill. Some red-tinged mining waste can be seen midway down the slope. The butte is capped by a tongue-shaped trachyte intrusion, 36 million years old, intruded into Pen Formation strata and the source of mercury bearing fluids. The mine was the last functioning mercury mine in the Terlingua mining district. It closed in 1972.

At the intersection of Highways 118 and 170, turn left for Terlingua, Lajitas and the river road to Presidio. Keep on Highway 118 for Alpine.

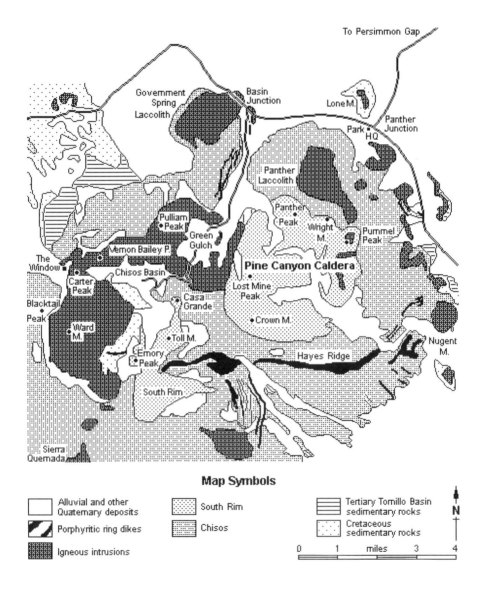

Geology: Basin Junction to Chisos Basin

Basin Junction – Chisos Basin

6 Miles

This route ascends from Basin Junction (4,008 feet) up through Green Gulch, a beautiful canyon carved in the flank of Pulliam Peak. As the road climbs, desert plant species give way to woodland species such as oak, juniper and pinon pine. The road reaches its summit at Panther Pass (5,800 feet) at the parking area for Lost Mine Trail. It then descends by a series of sharp switchbacks to the Chisos Basin (5,100 feet). The road is on volcanic and intrusive rocks the entire way.

The Chisos Mountains are a remnant of volcanic Chisos and South Rim Formation strata standing 5,000 feet above Tornillo Creek to the north and nearly 6,000 feet above the Rio Grande to the south. This enormous mountain block has a long history. It begins during the Laramide Orogeny when an anticline developed along a northwest-southeast axis in line with similar anticlines at Mariscal Mountain and the Christmas Mountains (see map on page 98). The Tertiary beds of the Tornillo Basin would have lapped up against it. They were followed by 3,500 feet of mainly ash-flow deposits of the Chisos Formation described on page 80.

After a period during which further uplift and some erosion took place, South Rim Formation pyroclastic flows erupted between 31.7 and 32.9 Ma from a small volcanic center in the high Chisos Mountains and from a number of volcanic vents just west of the Pine Canyon Caldera. This episode culminated with the collapse of the volcanic center into a small caldera, the Pine Canyon Caldera, and with volcanic domes forming on Lost Mine Peak in the caldera, and on vents at Casa Grande, Toll Mountain and Emory Peak west of the caldera. Finally, the Chisos Mountains pluton of granite and quartz syenite was intruded west of the Casa Grande-Emory Peak ridge, bringing up Boquillas and Aguja beds at least 2,000 feet above their normal level. The anticline's height is difficult to estimate; its top is covered. However, the Aguja-Javelina boundary is 900 feet higher at Santa Elena Junction than at Tornillo Creek so it is at least that high.

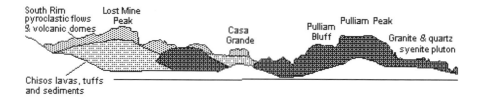

A Chisos Mountains panorama from Mile 1.5 on the Chisos Basin road

Erosion-resistant South Rim welded tuffs and lavas combined with the anticline have made the Chisos Mountains the dominant landform they are today.

On the map on page 140, the Pine Canyon caldera boundary roughly follows the circular outcrop of South Rim strata east of Green Gulch, from Panther Peak to Pummel Peak, then round to Crown Mountain and Lost Mine Peak and back to Panther Peak. The volcanic domes of Emory Peak, Toll Mountain and Casa Grande, the highest summits in the mountains, are on a ridge just west of the caldera. South Rim projects out from the ridge as a plateau overlooking an escarpment 2,500 feet high. The pluton has been uncovered and eroded into the spectacular shapes of Ward Mountain and Vernon Bailey Peak.

Mileposts on this segment are numbered from Basin Junction. Strata along the route are described in the table on pages 76-7.

Pine Canyon Caldera

At the junction, turn south towards the Chisos Basin. Pulliam Bluff (6,805 feet) rises 2,600 feet above the road on the right, part of the Chisos Mountains pluton. Note the profile of Alsate, an Apache chief. Legend says that when he was killed, the earth shook and his face appeared on the side of the mountain. The craggy, crenellated top of Pulliam Peak (6,870 feet), also part of the pluton, is visible beyond Pulliam Bluff.

Four porphyritic rhyolite dikes each about 25 feet wide run parallel to the road on the right for the next 1½ miles. They are a sector of the ring dike around the Pine Canyon caldera shown on the map on page 140. This discontinuous body is best developed at Hayes Ridge in a thick dike 5 miles long that intrudes the Lost Mine South Rim member. David Ogley proposed that the ring dike segments were feeders to the youngest South Rim member, the Burro Mesa member.

At the observation point at Mile 1, Casa Grande (7,325 feet) is straight ahead. The name, Spanish for Big House, probably refers to its massive profile. It rises above wooded slopes to a square-topped tower of bare rock with sheer cliffs, a volcanic dome of pinkish quartz trachyte, porphyritic in places, belonging to the Lost Mine Member of the South Rim Formation. A similar dome caps Lost Mine Peak (7,535 feet) at 10 o'clock. At 9 o'clock, the butte-like Panther Peak (6,409 feet) rises 1,750 feet above us, capped by ash-flow tuff of the Pine Canyon Rhyolite.

Willow and madrone trees grow beside the road a half-mile ahead. At 11 o'clock, Chisos Formation tuffs crop out in the foreground. The brown rock on the low skyline at 9 o'clock is Panther Laccolith, a porphyritic rhyolite intrusion. On the high skyline at 10:30 o'clock, Pummel Peak (6,620 feet), and Wright Peak (5,760 feet), the red peak in front, are almost in line. The latter is capped by ash-flow tuff of the Pine Canyon Rhyolite. At its summit, Pummel Peak has a porphyritic rhyolite plug 350 yards in diameter intruded into ash-flow tuff.

At Mile 3, note the black stains of desert varnish on the face of Pulliam Bluff, the bluff below Pulliam Peak at 3 o'clock. Desert varnish is common throughout the Big Bend and forms when water evaporates and leaves a residue of manganese and iron oxides on rock surfaces. The road at this point is in Green Gulch, a canyon in the Chisos Mountains pluton. The pluton is on both sides of the road for the next 2 miles.

A parking area and exhibit on the tree zone is at Mile 4.3. A half-mile ahead, the road goes through a narrow gap between jagged pinnacles on both sides of the road.

The parking area at Panther Pass (5,800 feet) is at the top of the divide between Green Gulch and the Basin. The view at right front is spectacular down to the campsite and beyond it to The Window. At 3 o'clock, the heavily jointed Pulliam Peak is breaking up rapidly. The Chisos Mountains pluton changes character east of Vernon Bailey Peak, becoming more jointed. Weathering along large joint surfaces has produced columns, pinnacles, spires and buttresses, giving it a much rougher profile than the smooth profiles of Vernon Bailey Peak and Ward Mountain.

Steeply bedded Chisos tuffs crop out beside the road and, straight ahead below Casa Grande, rhyolite dikes intrude Chisos tuffs. On the left, a trail leads to Lost Mine Peak. The full trail is quite demanding but you get an excellent view south into Mexico and down Juniper Canyon from a saddle a relatively easy mile up the trail.

Another splendid view of Casa Grande is on the left. It rises in wooded slopes to a tremendous square-topped monolith of bare rock with sheer, towering cliffs overlooking the visitor center in the basin some 2,000 feet below. The volcanic dome capping the mountain is slow to erode, and forms solid cliffs. Below it, thinly layered lava flows and air fall tuffs of the Chisos Formation erode more easily and form gentler slopes.

Casa Grande from The Window viewpoint (see also photograph on page 194)

Vegetation on its lower slopes is mainly juniper, oak, and piñon, a combination found at higher elevations in many of the mountainous areas of the Trans-Pecos region. Some Douglas firs also grow on the upper slopes of the northeast side of the mountain.

The road winds down into the basin along steep curves. Just before Mile 5.8, more Chisos tuff is exposed on the left. At Mile 5.9, the Basin comes into view again. Its appearance reminds many people of a volcanic crater but it is just the result of erosion. The Chisos Mountains pluton, as it ascended, brought up Cretaceous strata with it and perhaps some Chisos tuffs. South Rim strata, if they extended over the Basin, would have been broken up.

The soft Aguja and Boquillas beds eroded as The Window developed. The Window is a water gap created along jointing in the Chisos Mountains pluton, jointing parallel to mineral lineation in the intrusion. Mineral lineation occurs when platy minerals line up in a common orientation, perhaps from pressure, and result in weakened zones in the rock. The Window provided an exit for eroded material; the Basin is now about 2,000 feet below the general level of the surrounding mountaintops, and is still eroding down. Erosion is creating a similar gap at Panther Pass, already 1,000 to 1,500 feet below the tops on either side.

At the intersection at Mile 6.2, turn right to the campground or left to the visitor center, camper store and Chisos Mountains Lodge. Going up the hill to the visitor center, two rhyolite dikes in the Chisos Formation crop out in the ridge at 3 o'clock, another part of the Pine Canyon caldera ring dike. The visitor center, lodge and camper store are at Mile 6.4, an excellent viewpoint for the mountains around the basin (photographs on page 194).

Ross Maxwell Drive – Old Maverick Road

45 Miles

Ross Maxwell Drive is named for the noted geologist, the National Park's first superintendent, and 20 years later, the principal author of the only comprehensive book published on the park's geology. The Drive branches off the Panther Junction – Study Butte road at Santa Elena Junction, 13 miles west of Panther Junction, and ends after 32 miles at Santa Elena Canyon. From there, you can either retrace your steps or take Old Maverick Road to Maverick Junction, 13 miles of gravel road. It is usually in good condition but can be washed out by heavy rains so check at Park Headquarters before deciding to use it. This section combines descriptions of both roads.

The route begins by following the valley of Cottonwood Creek for 8 miles, rising 1,000 feet to the Sotol Vista viewpoint. Here, a saddle between Burro Mesa and the Chisos Mountains gives unsurpassed views over the Rio Grande valley below, from Punta de la Sierra to Lajitas, 50 miles to the west. From Sotol Vista, the road goes down a steep hill through conglomerate to a lower pediment cut in volcanic strata. It then descends gradually through basin fill and volcanic strata between lava-capped peaks to Castolon at Mile 22. From Castolon, the drive follows the Rio Grande west for 10 miles to Santa Elena Canyon along the magnificent Sierra Ponce-Mesa de Anguila escarpment, 1,500 feet high, the western boundary of Castolon Graben and the Sunken Block.

Old Maverick Road turns off just beyond the Canyon overlook. It follows Terlingua Creek for a few miles before turning northeast across Alamo Creek to climb on to the gravel hills that lie between Burro Mesa and the Rattlesnake Mountains. Intrusions and volcanic remnants create scattered hills but the overwhelming impression is of desert badlands. It has its own special beauty, however, particularly in the morning or late in the afternoon when the desert colors are accentuated and the badlands are less harsh than under the midday sun.

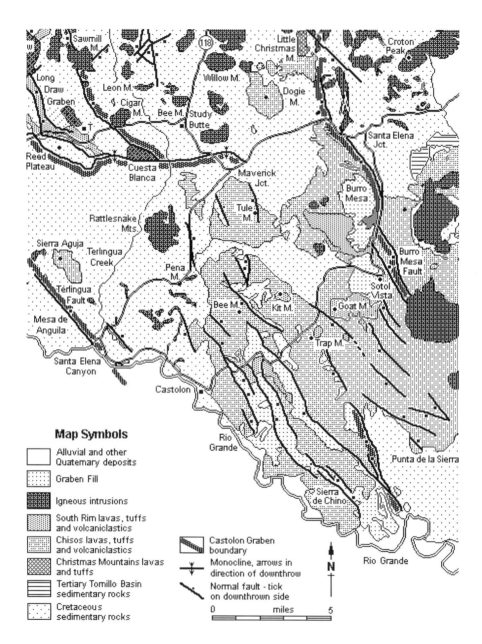

Map Symbols

☐ Alluvial and other Quaternary deposits

▦ Graben Fill

▦ Igneous intrusions

▦ South Rim lavas, tuffs and volcaniclastics

▦ Chisos lavas, tuffs and volcaniclastics

▦ Christmas Mountains lavas and tuffs

☰ Tertiary Tomillo Basin sedimentary rocks

☐ Cretaceous sedimentary rocks

▱ Castolon Graben boundary

⟂ Monocline, arrows in direction of downthrow

╲ Normal fault - tick on downthrown side

0   miles   5

N

Geology: Ross Maxwell Scenic Drive

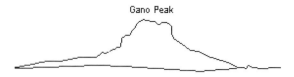

Gano Peak is a trachytic porphyry plug left of the road at Mile 1. It may be the eroded neck of a volcanic vent.

Turn left at Santa Elena Junction on to Ross Maxwell Scenic Drive. Mileposts are numbered from the junction to Cottonwood Campground at Mile 23½. Numbering of mileposts begins again at Cottonwood Campground and continues along the 8½ miles to Santa Elena Canyon. Old Maverick Road does not have mileposts; distances are measured from Santa Elena Canyon overlook. Strata along the route are described in the table on pages 76-7.

Castolon Graben and the Burro Mesa Fault

The Scenic Drive runs parallel to the Burro Mesa fault zone to Sotol Vista, 8 miles ahead. The fault is part of the eastern boundary of the Castolon Graben that, with its northern continuation, the Cigar Mountain Graben, runs south southeast from the Christmas Mountains to the Rio Grande, and continues another 30 miles into Mexico (see map on page 98). The boundary begins with a series of parallel faults stepping across from a major fault on the west face of the Christmas Mountains and continues with the Burro Mesa fault zone as far as Sierra Quemada. It continues across another set of parallel faults south of Sierra Quemada and crosses the Rio Grande due south of Sotol Vista. The Burro Mesa fault zone has a displacement of about 1,500 feet to the right midway along the mesa.

The western boundary of the Castolon Graben is the Terlingua Fault, which crosses into the United States at Santa Elena Canyon. Downthrow at the canyon is 2,900 feet. There are several small grabens within the main graben, in which strata have been further displaced as much as 1,800 feet and in which Delaho Formation conglomerates, sandstones, and siltstones have been preserved.

Santa Elena Junction to Sotol Vista

For the first five miles from Santa Elena Junction, the road follows the attractive valley of Cottonwood Creek, which in turn runs along the Burro Mesa fault zone. The fault zone is the low point in the terrain, probably because rocks are broken up along it, making them easier to erode.

Crumpled Chisos tuff beds on either side of Burro Mesa Fault on mountain face as seen from Mile 5.5.

The notch in the Chisos Mountains at about 2 o'clock from the Chisos Mountains Exhibit is The Window, through which the Chisos Basin drains (photograph on page 195). Casa Grande is on the skyline behind The Window, a volcanic dome; Pulliam and Vernon Bailey Peaks to its left and Carter Peak and Ward Mountain to its right are all part of the intrusive Chisos Mountains pluton.

For its first 3 miles, the Scenic Drive is on alluvium over Javelina Formation variegated non-marine claystones, which extend across the flat towards The Window for about 2 miles. There they disappear under about 600 feet of Canoe Formation mudstone and claystone. These in turn are overlain by stratified Chisos Formation volcanic tuffs, which create gray streaks in the face below The Window.

Burro Mesa, although on the downside of the Burro Mesa fault zone rises up to 1,000 feet above the creek valley. Much of the mesa is covered by Fingers Formation conglomerate and sandstone, underlain by Burro Mesa rhyolite. Several volcanic vents have recently been discovered on the mesa which sourced the Burro Mesa rhyolite and capped the mesa, thus making it more resistant to erosion. The area between Cottonwood Creek and the Chisos Mountains pluton probably never had a South Rim cover leaving the unprotected Chisos tuffs to be eroded away.

At Mile 3.5, a fault, an offshoot of the Burro Mesa fault zone, crosses the road at a fault scarp just beyond the Sam Nail Ranch Exhibit. It displaces strata down the scarp so that from this point on, the Javelina claystones are buried under Chisos Formation tuffs and lavas.

The Fins of Fire Exhibit on the left at Mile 4 describes the three dikes cutting across the hillside at 9 o'clock. Dikes, being narrow, cool quickly and are fine grained. They do not erode easily and tend to stand up above the terrain. At about Mile 5.5 crumpled beds of Chisos tuff and lava can be seen in the mountain face at 11 o'clock as shown in the diagram above and in the photograph on page 195. A fault in the Burro Mesa zone runs up the mountainside in a shallow gully and disappears from view in a notch on the skyline. Chisos strata dip down to the fault on either side.

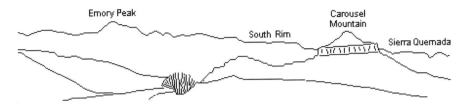

The view to the east from Sotol Vista Overlook; in Carousel Peak a resistant lava bed has created a collar.

At 5 o'clock from the parking area at the high point on the road over Burro Mesa, you can see Burro Mesa rhyolite up to 500 feet thick on the mesa overlying yellow Wasp Spring flow breccia (see following page). On the left, several hills stand more than 1,000 feet above the road where thick Tule Mountain lava beds on their summits have slowed down erosion. The Tule Mountain member, 350 feet thick, is an erosion-resistant porphyritic lava, ranging in composition from trachyte to trachybasalt (see diagram on page 21), and is found from Punta de la Sierra south of the Chisos Mountains to as far west as the Bofecillos Mountains. It rests on eroded Chisos tuffs and probably came from multiple sources, perhaps including the Sierra Rica caldera, south of Lajitas.

The Blue Creek Ranch Overlook on the left provides fine views of the southern Chisos Mountains. The highest point, the volcanic dome of Emory Peak (7,825 feet) is at 7 o'clock. Ward Mountain at 5:30 o'clock is part of the Chisos Mountains pluton and is pinkish compared to the gray volcanic dome. Carousel Mountain (4,817 feet) at 9 o'clock is a good example of a volcanic outlier in a fairly advanced state of erosion. Eventually, the upper resistant bed of Tule Mountain lava will wear away, and the mountain will become a true pyramid, at least for a time.

Sotol Point Overlook

It is well worth the time to take the short diversion to Sotol Vista Overlook and examine the splendid panorama it provides over the western park. Looking west along the parking area parapet towards Lajitas and taking it as 12 o'clock, the Rio Grande is from 8:30 to 12 o'clock, 2,300 feet below. The eastern boundary of the Castolon Graben runs down to the river at about 9 o'clock (see geological map on page 146). Santa Elena Canyon at 11:30 o'clock cuts through the Terlingua Fault escarpment on the western boundary of the Castolon Graben. On a clear day, Lajitas Mesa can be seen as the high gray mesa in the far distance at about 12 o'clock, 25 miles away. The dark volcanic mountains just below the overlook at 10:30 o'clock are capped by durable Burro Mesa rhyolite and are described later.

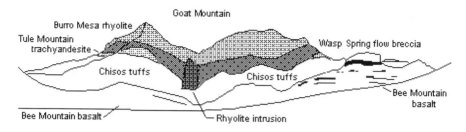

Goat Mountain from the Goat Mountain exhibit

Beyond them, the light gray butte at 11:00 o'clock is Cerro Castellan, a roadside landmark. The Rattlesnake Mountains at 12:30 o'clock are a rugged, roughly circular group of peaks straddling the park boundary, and are eroded from a gabbro sill about 28 million years old.

Burro Mesa at 1 o'clock is capped by Burro Mesa rhyolite, overlying yellow Wasp Spring flow breccia. The Chisos-South Rim contact is at the base of the yellow band. The other mountains nearby are identified in the exhibit. The Christmas Mountains are on the skyline at 2:00 o'clock with Little Christmas Mountain below them and the Corazones Peaks to their right. Santiago Peak is the flat-topped mountain on the right flank of East Corazon Peak, 43 miles away. Croton Peak is at 3 o'clock. The Santiago-Dead Horse Mountains are on the distant skyline to the right of Croton Peak.

The Chisos Mountains rise dramatically above the overlook, the highest point being the volcanic dome of Emory Peak (7,825 feet) at 5 o'clock (photograph on page 196). The forbidding mountainous terrain of Sierra Quemada (6,040 feet) can just be glimpsed at 7 o'clock, 1,800 feet above the road. It is the site of the circular Sierra Quemada caldera, 2½ miles in diameter, the source of the Mule Ear Spring tuff. The caldera's northwestern rim of porphyritic trachyte faces the overlook.

Downhill through the Fingers Formation

Just beyond the Sotol Vista turnoff, the road winds steeply down hill through piles of coarse boulders and gravel of the Fingers Formation, poorly cemented material mainly derived from Chisos strata. The formation is about 2½ million years old at its base and was created before the Rio Grande developed its present course. It covers most of the eastern part of Burro Mesa and it reaches an elevation of 4,082 feet at the high point on the mesa. Its upper surface is an erosion surface, however, so at one time it was thicker than now and would have partly buried the Chisos

Mountains. Light gray Chisos tuffs crop out below the formation at the bottom of the hill.

About a mile and a half ahead, the Burro Mesa Pour-off road is on the right, almost exactly 1,000 feet below Sotol Vista Overlook. Fine yellow cliffs of Wasp Spring pyroclastics under a Burro Mesa rhyolite cap dip steeply into the pour-off on both sides (photograph on page 197). At one time, geologists thought that these rocks in the southwest Park were produced by the Pine Canyon caldera, but recent mapping shows that they came from nearby individual vents. Three, including the Burro Mesa pour-off vent, have been discovered on Burro Mesa, and others occur on Goat, Kit and Trap Mountains, and Cerro Castellan.

The cliffs at the pour-off and on the face of Goat Mountain are vertical sections across two such vents. Development of a vent began with explosions that created around it pyroclastic surge deposits and flow breccia, the Wasp Spring flow breccia. In some places, the deposits were hot enough to weld together; in other places they remain as loose debris. The Burro Mesa lava then erupted through the surge deposits and flow breccia from a feeder dike, sometimes exploding into a myriad of small fragments that welded together. A strongly welded pyroclastic flow is often very difficult to distinguish from lava. The Bureau of Economic Geology has published a guidebook to Tuff Canyon by Daniel Barker, which gives comprehensive descriptions of these units (see Reading List). Light gray tuff crops out on the slopes left of the pour-off behind a dark porphyritic rhyolite plug.

Goat (4,625 feet) on the left and Kit Mountains (3,825 feet) on the right straddle the road 2 miles from the Pour-off road junction. Trap Mountain (4,125 feet) is another mile along on the right. All three have volcanic vents that deposited Burro Mesa rhyolite flows and Wasp Spring pyroclastics on eroded surfaces of Chisos Formation tuffs and lavas. Thick lava flows around the vents have retarded erosion leaving the three peaks to rise between 1,000 and 2,000 feet above the road, steep-sided and dark, making for a dramatic volcanic landscape. The name Trap is a mining term for fine-grained dark rocks.

The parking area for the Chimneys Trail is at Mile 11.8. This trail follows an old road to Old Maverick Road. The Chimneys are three volcanic necks that form a ridge about 2½ miles beyond Kit Mountain at 3 o'clock. Lajitas Mesa is on the skyline beyond them. Tule Mountain is about 4:30 o'clock, a volcanic outlier. The sharp cupola of Dominguez Mountain (5,157 feet), a complex intrusion with an associated dike swarm, is on the skyline at 9 o'clock.

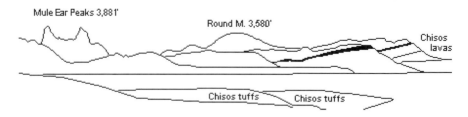

The panorama from the Mule Ear Peaks Overlook (photograph on page 196)

The Goat Mountain exhibit is at Mile 13.9. Here, erosion has uncovered a volcanic vent in Chisos tuffs in a setting very similar to the Burro Mesa Pour-off. The brown rhyolite plug near the base of the hill is a volcanic neck (see diagram on page 150). The V-shaped profile in the Chisos tuffs and lavas on Goat Mountain has been carved out by the volcanic eruption. Burro Mesa rhyolite and Wasp Spring pyroclastics overlay the Chisos strata. In the foreground, black Bee Mountain basalt beds crop out in a low ridge.

A fault crosses the road just before Mile 14 and runs along the right side of Kit Mountain and downthrows strata 800 feet to the right, lowering Kit and Trap Mountains. The road, which has been on a pediment since the base of the hill below Sotol Vista, descends 200 feet down this fault scarp through pinkish pediment gravels deposited on Chisos Formation strata. This is the first of several faults that we will cross along the road to Castolon, all roughly parallel to this one, that displace strata down into the Castolon Graben.

The Mule Ear Overlook is a good viewpoint for the southern Park. The Mule Ear Peaks (3,881 feet) are two eroded dikes standing up above Chisos Formation tuffs. Directly to their right Round Mountain (3,580 feet) is capped by Burro Mesa rhyolite and Wasp Spring flow breccia and is probably the site of another volcanic vent. Chisos lavas and tuffs crop out on the escarpment to the right of Round Mountain and dip under South Rim strata on Round Mountain. Hard Chisos lavas, Tule Mountain trachyandesite and Mule Ear Spring tuff among others, have created a resistant layer that is eroding back in an escarpment from the Rio Grande valley. The lower ground at the base of the 650-feet escarpment and in front of the Overlook is underlain by soft tuffs, some of which crop out in the immediate foreground. Trap Mountain looms above the overlook on the left.

Tertiary Tornillo Basin strata are missing in this area of the Park so Chisos tuffs directly overlie multicolored Cretaceous-age Javelina claystones and crop out along the road for the next two miles or so. Rhyolite outliers overlying the tuff form ragged brown hills. Several rhyolite plugs and dikes intruded into Javelina Formation strata create buttes and pyramids on either side of the road. These rhyolite bodies have been dated at 28 Ma, slightly younger than the Burro Mesa rhyolites (29 Ma).

A mile ahead, a roadcut exposes Alamo Creek basalt at the base of the Chisos Formation overlying Javelina claystones.

Castolon Sub-Graben

Going through a dry wash at Mile 17.5, the road crosses a fault hidden in the alluvium at roadside. It displaces strata 1,800 feet down to 12 o'clock and is the eastern boundary of a sub-graben within the Castolon Graben; the western boundary fault of the sub-graben is about 3 miles ahead. Delaho Formation sandstones and conglomerates have been preserved in the sub-graben and crop out in roadcuts over the next 3 miles and, at mile 17.9, as stratified gravel exposed on the side of a butte. The Delaho Formation is as much as 23 million years old. The base of the Javelina Formation here is about 300 feet above sea level, some 3,000 feet below its level at Santa Elena Junction, and the lowest point in the Castolon Graben. Rhyolite bodies have been intruded along the fault and are found in the sedimentary rocks on either side of it. In places, high points in the rhyolite bodies break through the gravel blanket, mainly as ridges.

At the Tuff Canyon Exhibit, you can see how Blue Creek, last seen between Goat and Kit Mountains, has eroded the canyon down through pinkish Delaho gravels and silt, pyroclastic flows and surge-deposits, to dark erosion-resistant Bee Mountain basalt. A volcanic vent has been found about a mile east and is the probable source of the pyroclastic flows and surge deposits. Mammal bones of early Miocene camel, deer and rabbit have been found a mile down the Blue Creek valley at 10 o'clock.

The junction with the River Road is on the left at Mile 20.2. This road is quite passable by high clearance vehicles if not washed out by rains. Ask at the Park Headquarters about its condition before attempting to use it. If it is in good condition, it can be used to cross the southern Park to the Boquillas Canyon road near Rio Grande Village. It provides wonderful panoramic views of Punta de la Sierra, Sierra Quemada, the Chisos Mountains, Mariscal Mountain and into Mexico across the Rio Grande.

Shortly beyond the River Road junction, the road crosses the southwestern boundary fault of the sub-graben. This fault has a downthrow to the northeast of about 1,200 feet. Light gray Chisos Formation tuffs crop out on its upthrown side (photograph on page 197). At 1 o'clock, a volcanic spine protruding out of white tuff looks like a fossilized tree,

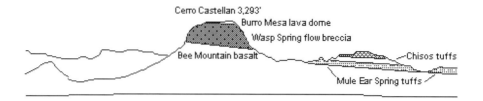

Cerro Castellan from the Desert Mountain Overlook (photograph on page 198)

including "grain" and a "knothole". The "grain" is actually flow structure created in the lava as it rose. The "knothole" is where a boulder has been weathered out. When the spine was first discovered, newspapers wrote about the "lost forest of Castolon".

Cerro Castellan

The Cerro Castellan Exhibit is at Mile 20.5. Cerro Castellan (3,293 feet) is a Burro Mesa volcanic vent, rising 1,030 feet above the road in a stack of red, orange and white Wasp Spring pyroclastic surge deposits capped by a small Burro Mesa rhyolite lava dome and underlain by Bee Mountain basalt. The rhyolite feeder crops out as a small ridge on the left at the base of the dome. The name Cerro Castellan seems to have been derived from Castolon, which in turn may have come from the name of an early resident named Castulo. On the right of the road, a number of small pipes and dikes of rhyolite create a peak with a sheer face. Reddish and light gray Chisos tuff is exposed at the roadside.

The high mesa across the Rio Grande is Sierra Ponce, a horst of lower Cretaceous limestones about 1,800 feet high. The upper half of the cliff is made up of beautiful pink and gray Santa Elena Limestone, followed by 300 feet of softer Sue Peaks Formation limestone and then Del Carmen limestone, the other hard limestone in the Lower Cretaceous. The Terlingua Fault, the southwestern boundary fault of the Castolon Graben continues along the escarpment base.

Castolon

The Castolon historic area is on the left a half-mile beyond the Cerro Castellan exhibit. Now a Park Ranger station and trading post, it began in 1903 as a farming community called Santa Helena, where settlers irrigated the fertile river bottomland and grew wheat, corn, oats, and other grains. Another group of immigrants settled at La Coyota on the west bank of Alamo Creek, two miles upstream. Eventually the area had some 200 or 300 residents, mainly subsistence farmers. The U.S. Army maintained a small garrison at Castolon during a period of border troubles from 1914 to 1916. A larger trading post opened in 1919 and commercial cotton farming began in the area in 1921, both under the control of Howard Perry, the owner of the Chisos Mine at Terlingua. A cotton gin was set up in the spring of 1923. In 1926, a post office was opened and marked the change of the community's name to Castolon; there was already a post office called Santa Helena. Though the cotton operation was never a major financial success, it was a steady source of local employment until it ended in 1942 when the Chisos Mine filed for bankruptcy. Today, the store is in the old cavalry barracks. The two houses were officers' quarters.

Along the River

Castolon is built on gravel banks of recent alluvium 50 feet above the river. The road continues on this alluvium along the river towards Santa Elena Canyon. The Cottonwood Campground road is on the left at Mile 22.5. Mileposts between here and the canyon are numbered from the campground. Desert Mountain Overlook is on the right just ahead. The Chisos Mountains show up well on the skyline to the northeast. Ward Mountain, Emory Peak and the South Rim stand out in particular (photograph on page 198). There are also fine views of the variegated light gray and pinkish cream limestones of Sierra Ponce across the river and of Cerro Castellan and its surroundings (photograph on page 198). Santa Elena Canyon is at 11 o'clock with Mesa de Anguila on its right.

Just beyond the overlook, the road goes through well-bedded yellowish Aguja claystones and sandstones. These follow the road on the right as far as the canyon. A pour-off cuts down the face of Sierra Ponce at Mile 4. A flood plain farming exhibit is at Mile 4.5. More recent gravel banks are on the right of the road for the next mile and the river flood plain on the left.

Santa Elena Canyon

The Santa Elena Canyon overlook and exhibit is at Mile 5.2. The canyon is about 8 miles long and 1,500 feet deep at its mouth. Along the river a mile below its entrance, a rockslide from the Mexican side known as the Labyrinth rises to a height of 180 feet above the river and creates a major navigational hazard for boaters. Below the rockslide the canyon is narrow, sometimes only twenty-five feet wide, and sheer.

The canyon was a fearsome obstacle to early explorers. In 1747, Governor Pedro de Rábago y Terán of Coahuila, leading an expedition into the Big Bend, tried to follow the Rio Grande, but had to go around the canyon. In the summer of 1860, an expedition of camels from Fort Davis under Lieutenant William Echols followed the Rio Grande from Lajitas to

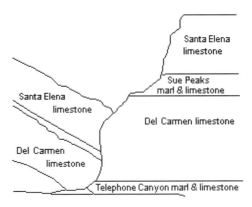

Santa Elena Canyon from the canyon overlook

the mouth of the canyon, which he called the Grand Puerta. The expedition then detoured northeast to Terlingua Creek and back down to the Rio Grande just below the canyon. More recently, however, and especially since the opening of the park in 1944, the canyon has become a popular recreational spot.

Looking at this tremendous cleft in very hard rock, the visitor can't help but wonder why the river should have taken this course rather than, say, flow along the base of Mesa de Anguila. The answer seems to be that it established its present course before the hard Santa Elena limestones of Mesa de Anguila became uncovered. Once established, a river channel is very difficult to change.

Let us review the evidence. The height of the land surface at the end of Chisos volcanic activity, 34 million years ago, can be estimated from the Chisos relics remaining. The upper surface of the Chisos strata on Cerro Castellan, for example, is about 2,850 feet above sea level. If you add back the 2,900 feet displacement on the Terlingua Fault at the canyon, the elevation of the top of the Chisos strata at the end of the volcanic period would have been around 5,750 feet. At Sierra Aguja, 3 miles northwest of the canyon mouth, the top of the Chisos Formation would have been 6,080 feet before the Terlingua Fault developed.

The Rio Conchos, which developed before the Rio Grande broke through from New Mexico, set its course on this surface, far above the present upper surfaces of Santa Elena limestone on Sierra Ponce and Mesa de Anguila, which are a little over 3,400 feet. It would have established a channel long before it had cut down to them.

Looking west along Mesa de Anguila and to Sierra Aguja from Santa Elena Canyon Overlook

Old Maverick Road

Old Maverick Road is a 13-mile improved gravel road usually open to all vehicles, but before using it check at park headquarters to determine its current condition. It offers attractive panoramas across the Castolon Graben to Burro Mesa and up to the Chisos Mountains. It also has the advantage of making the trip to Study Butte 25 miles shorter than if you retrace your steps to Santa Elena Junction.

The road begins by traveling across a ridge in Aguja and then Pen Formation rocks. The ridge is there because an olivine basalt sill intruded into the Pen strata on the right has retarded erosion. On the left across the Terlingua Creek valley, a similar intrusion crests another low ridge in Pen claystones. The road then veers to the right as it crosses a fault parallel to the Terlingua Fault and leaves the creek valley. This fault drops strata down about 1,300 feet to the northeast.

The turnoff to the ruins of the abandoned settlement of Terlingua Abaja is 2 miles along on the left. Mexican immigrants had established a settlement here called Terlingua well before the discovery of mercury in the area in the late nineteenth century. In 1903, the Chisos Mining Company began operations about eight miles north, and the town that grew up around it came to be known as Terlingua; the original Mexican settlement then was called *Terlingua Abaja* (more properly Terlingua Abajo), Lower Terlingua.

Sierra Aguja (3,280 feet), Needle Peak in Spanish, is the sharp peak at 3 o'clock, a Chisos Formation outlier in Javelina Formation mudstones. A small outcrop of Tule Mountain Trachyandesite at its summit has held back erosion and created the sharp profile. Note the light-colored Chisos tuff in its lower slopes.

Just beyond the turnoff, the road crosses a line of Aguja hills capped by remnants of another olivine basalt sill. Slickrock Mountain, with a very sheer cliff on its left, is at 12 o'clock on the skyline. At 3 o'clock, Bee Mountain (3,400 feet) stands up sharply above the desert floor, a Chisos Formation outlier similar to Sierra Aguja. This Bee Mountain is not to be confused with the Bee Mountain near Study Butte.

The road crosses another fault parallel to the Terlingua Fault at Mile 4, one of the faults on the western boundary the Castolon sub-graben we crossed earlier (see page 153). The sub-graben shallows to the north and disappears before it reaches Old Maverick Road but the faults continue to the vicinity of the road (see geological map on page 146). Yellowish Aguja sandstone on the left is down faulted against gray Pen Formation mudstones on the right. Crossing the dry wash of Alamo Creek, Aguja sandstones and claystones form badlands on the left. To the right, below Peña Mountain, Luna's Jacal is a National Register site. It was the home of Gilberto Luna, a Mexican born in Durango. He entered the United States in 1901 and lived here 25 or 30 years with his sixth wife, with whom he had 10 children. He died in 1947 at the age of 108. He is said to have had 48 children in all.

Peña Mountain rises steeply 300 feet above the jacal. It is part of a laccolith, a trachyte intrusion into Aguja strata about 125 feet thick. The main body is very similar to the intrusion at the Rattlesnake Mountains, three miles northwest, and may even be part of the same intrusion that was brought to the surface here by faulting.

The Chimneys Trail turnoff is on the right just beyond Peña Mountain. The trail passes by The Chimneys, a ridge of rhyolite volcanic necks, across the pediment to Ross Maxwell Drive. The Maverick road runs along Alamo Creek for the next mile and then follows another fault for a further mile. Along this straight, Javelina strata are on the right on the downthrow side, Aguja strata on the left. Trees mark the fault trace, as in many places in the Big Bend. Broken rock along faults provides channels for water to rise to the surface; trees grow where water is present. At about Mile 8, the fault can be seen about 10 yards off the road on the left. Twelve inches wide, it down faults purplish gray Javelina mudstones against yellow Aguja sandstones.

At Mile 9, the road climbs gradually out of the Alamo Creek valley through roadcuts in gravel banks on to a gravel pediment 180 feet above. Underlying Javelina mudstones crop out in places through the thin gravel layer. The top of the pediment is an excellent viewpoint. Maverick Mountain is at 10 o'clock with Willow Mountain to its rear. The Christmas Mountains and Little Christmas Mountain are at 11 o'clock, Slickrock Mountain at 1 o'clock, and Tule Mountain at 2 o'clock with the Chisos Mountains behind it. The skyline to the right of the Chisos Mountains is stepped down stair-like to the right by faults on the eastern boundary of the Castolon Graben between Sotol Vista and Punta de la Sierra.

The junction with an old road to Terlingua is at Mile 10. The Rattlesnake Mountains (2,911 feet) are at 8 o'clock from the junction. They are a rugged, roughly circular group of peaks that straddle the boundary of the National Park, about 450 feet above the road at their highest point. They have been eroded from a trachyte laccolith which intruded Aguja mudstones and sandstones 29 million years ago. On the western face, away from the road, the intrusion has been eroded into a steep cliff and its upper surface is well exposed.

The road leaves Javelina strata just after the old Terlingua road turnoff and for the remainder of the route is on a gravel pediment overlying Chisos tuffs and lavas. Tule Mountain (3,838 feet) is the distinctive butte at 3 o'clock 1,200 feet above the road. The low hills in the foreground are capped by remnants of Ash Spring basalt which overlay air-fall tuffs that came from the Christmas Mountains calderas. Arroyos on both sides of the road have white or very light gray tuff exposures in their banks.

At Maverick Junction, turn left for Study Butte or right for Panther Junction.

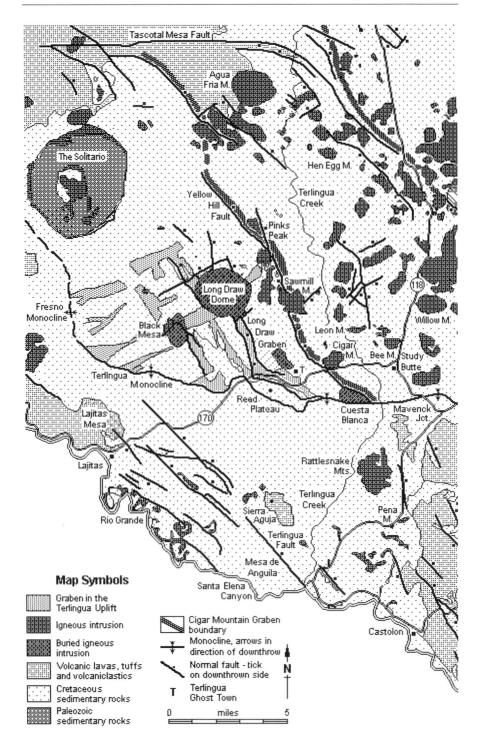

Geology: Study Butte to Lajitas along FM 170

FM 170 Study Butte – Lajitas

18 Miles

Highway 170 between Study Butte and Lajitas roughly parallels the Terlingua Uplift, which provides attractive mountain scenery to the north. To the south, fine vistas range across the Castolon Graben lowlands and the Terlingua Creek valley to the magnificent limestone escarpment of Mesa de Anguila. Lajitas is a former border crossing point on the Rio Grande, now the site of an ambitious program to develop a resort on the river. Highway 170 continues from Lajitas to Presidio, 50 miles west, along the dramatic river road through Big Bend Ranch State Park.

The area has a colorful history. It was the site of a prospecting frenzy around 1888 when cinnabar, the ore for mercury, was discovered in commercial quantities on California Hill and attracted great numbers of prospectors. Mining was the principal industry in the area until the 1940s when the largest mine went bankrupt. Sporadic mining continued until the early 1970s by which time tourism had become the mainstay of the local economy, as it remains.

The section begins at the junction of FM 170 and Highway 118 in Study Butte and mileages are measured from this point. Strata along the route are described in the table on pages 76-7.

Study Butte Mine

Study Butte and Terlingua owe their existence to mercury mining. Cinnabar, the ore of mercury was found in fractures in the intrusion that caps Study Butte, one mile south of the FM 170 junction (see page 139). High-grade ore mostly occurred near contacts with sedimentary rocks or where fractures were concentrated. The Study Butte mine operated from 1905 to 1946, and again from 1970 to 1972, employing up to fifty people. By the time it finally closed, the town had taken on a new lease of life as a tourist point at the west entrance to Big Bend National Park .

Study Butte is in the Cigar Mountain Graben, a low-lying area between the Christmas Mountains and the Terlingua Uplift. The graben is a northern extension of the Castolon Graben described in the previous section. The two are separated by the Terlingua Monocline which runs east west before turning north around the Solitario. Geologists believe that the monocline is the result of strata being draped over a fault at the edge of the Chihuahua Trough. The trough ran inland from the Gulf of Mexico to El Paso and began subsiding in the late Jurassic era, about 150 million years ago (see page 73).

The graben is bordered on the east by faults along the Christmas Mountains, which bring strata 1,500 feet down into the graben. They merge into a series of northwest-southeast trending faults that cross Highway 118 north of Study Butte (see Study Butte – Alpine section). The graben's western boundary is the Yellow Hill Fault, which fades into the Tascotal Mesa Fault at Agua Fria Mountain. Maximum displacement on the Yellow Hill Fault is 1,000 feet near Pinks Peak. It dies away into the Terlingua Monocline at Cuesta Blanca.

Volcanic strata are absent in the Cigar Mountain Graben and except for outliers around Terlingua Abaja and around Sierra Aguja are also absent in the Castolon Graben. Sierra Aguja is made up of about 700 feet of Chisos tuffs and lavas, capped by Tule Mountain Trachyandesite, a similar sequence to Lajitas Mesa, so it seems likely that Chisos strata were initially continuous across the graben. Erosion in both grabens is controlled by Terlingua Creek and has now reached the level where Chisos strata has been mostly removed and Aguja, Pen and Boquillas sedimentary rocks are under attack.

At the town of Study Butte Pen Formation claystones and alluvium cover the graben floor. The claystones erode into badlands such as those at the foot of Bee Mountain (3,452 feet) at 3 o'clock. The mountain is a trachyte intrusion, red, striated and jagged, with a fine 850-foot cliff facing the road. The beautifully striated Willow Mountain is behind it to its right. About a half-mile from the Highway 118 junction, the road descends on to Boquillas Formation flagstones underlying the Pen claystones. The flagstones break up into rubble, which litters the terrain.

Cuesta Blanca at 10 o'clock is a Boquillas limestone hill standing 250 feet above the badlands around it. It conceals an intrusion that baked and hardened the overlying limestones, slowing down erosion. The Yellow Hill Fault has created an escarpment on the northeast face of the hill and intersects the Terlingua Monocline at its southeast corner.

A mile from Study Butte, the road goes down steeply into the valley of Terlingua Creek, a dry wash most of the year. The creek is the major tributary of the Rio Grande between Alamito Creek, 60 miles west, and Maravillas Creek, 50 miles east, rising 50 miles northeast of Study Butte and draining 1,315 square miles. It has created a 180-foot deep valley from the vicinity of Hen Egg Mountain, 12 miles to the north, to its mouth at the

Rio Grande, 10 miles to the south. At roadside, bluffs of finely bedded cream-colored Boquillas limestone rise above the channel (photograph on page 200).

A mile west of the creek, the adobe ruins of the 248 Mine are on the right. Cinnabar was found there in small separate ore bodies at the margins of a vertical breccia-filled pipe and in fractures in the pipe. Breccia pipes develop when limestone dissolves in water creating caverns; the caverns collapse and fill up with breccia, a mixture of broken rock and rubble. The pipe in the 248 Mine is roughly circular at the surface with a diameter of 115 feet. It was mined down to 800 feet below the surface.

The mine was notorious for the high asphalt content in its ore. The asphalt was brought in from the surrounding Boquillas limestones by the mineralizing fluids that brought in the cinnabar. Cinnabar was processed by heating it to 360° F. in furnaces to release mercury vapor, which was condensed and captured in condensers. The asphalt saved on fuel cost but unfortunately tended to explode when heated and made the ore difficult to process. The mine's wooden head frame was struck by lightning in 1981 and caught on fire. The fire spread to the underground workings. No one took the fire seriously until the tarmac on Highway 170 began to melt and run downhill 2 years later. It was then put out.

Cigar Mountain (3,301 feet) is on the right of the road 2 miles from Terlingua Creek, a circular intrusion 360 feet thick. Leon Mountain (3,062 feet), the low dark ridge about a mile away at 4 o'clock, is a 300-feet thick sill in Pen mudstones. The two intrusions may have been a single intrusion at one time, now cut in two by Terlingua Creek. A feeder vent has been found at the west end of Leon Mountain. Both intrusions are composed of dark basalt, which weathers to a dark gray color in contrast to the reddish weathered surfaces of the trachyte intrusions near Study Butte such as Bee Mountain.

The Terlingua Uplift

Just after Fulcher Road on the left Highway 170 climbs 120 feet up the fault scarp of the Yellow Hill Fault on to the Terlingua Uplift. The Uplift and its continuation to the north, the Solitario, form an oblong 18 miles northwest southwest and 14 miles across. The Terlingua Monocline forms its southern boundary; strata are downthrown as much as 1,500 feet to the south. The Fresno Monocline forms its western boundary where strata are downthrown 500 to 800 feet to the west. The eastern boundary is the Yellow Hill Fault. The block fades into the Tascotal Mesa Fault northwards.

The view up Terlingua Creek from near Terlingua Ghost Town exit

The Solitario was created by a laccolith that domed the rocks above. The dome's summit was later eroded away, creating a rim 8 miles in diameter and a central basin 5 miles across. The rim can be seen from Highway 170 near Lajitas, its Cretaceous limestone flatirons dipping towards the road. Paleozoic rocks like those of the Marathon Basin crop out in the central basin; part of the laccolith is also exposed. The Solitario is in Big Bend Ranch State Park; the Bureau of Economic Geology has published an excellent guidebook to the park that describes the Solitario in detail (see Reading List).

Early geologists thought the entire Terlingua Uplift was created by an intrusion, but more recent studies show it to be a Laramide structure. The area between the Terlingua Monocline and the Tascotal Mesa Fault was arched and extended to the northwest by compression from the east-northeast between 68 to 50 Ma, producing the uplift and a series of east-northeast trending grabens (see map on page 160). Igneous intrusions came later and introduced cinnabar along faults and fractures parallel to the grabens. The local intrusions that have been dated include Sawmill Mountain, 44 Ma, the Solitario, 38 Ma and Black Mesa, 34.5 Ma.

At about 24 Ma, Basin and Range extension began wrenching strata north of the Tascotal Mesa Fault to the west in relation to strata to the south of the fault. An intrusion on the fault north of the Solitario shows that a half-mile of movement took place there. This wrenching created another set of grabens trending north-northwest, the largest being Long Draw Graben. Subsequent erosion stripped off the upper strata down to the Santa Elena Limestone, which caps the uplift today except in the grabens, where Buda, Del Rio, Boquillas and Pen strata still remain.

South County Road on the right is the old Terlingua-Alpine road, now a Brewster County road open to the public for 5.6 miles. The spectacular cleft of Santa Elena Canyon in the Mesa de Anguila cliff face is at 9:30 o'clock, 11 miles away. Looking back toward the Park, the Chisos Mountains are on the skyline at 6:30 o'clock; Casa Grande is in the middle with Emory Peak to its right. From this viewpoint, the mountains look like an uplifted block but although there has been a certain amount of doming in the underlying Cretaceous strata, the left escarpment is the result of erosion. The right escarpment includes a series of fault scarps.

Sawmill Mountain (3,750 feet) is the prominent hill at 2 o'clock from Terlingua Ghost Town exit, a porphyritic trachyte plug 44 million years old. The Yellow Hill Fault runs between it and Pinks Peak (3,686 feet), the sharp pointed cone on its left flank, another trachyte plug.

Looking up Terlingua Creek valley, Hen Egg Mountain (5,005 feet), a rhyolite plug, is 10 miles away at 4 o'clock. It rises 2,000 feet above Terlingua Creek in front. Panther Mountain (4,331 feet), a similar plug, is just to its right. Aguja and some Pen strata crop out along the flat-bottomed Terlingua Creek valley. They have been eroded into steep-sided arroyos and into a channel 200 feet deep in places along the creek.

The Terlingua Mining Area

A half-mile beyond the ghost town exit, the road drops steeply into Long Draw Graben, descending 125 feet down the graben's northeast boundary fault scarp. The graben is 6 miles long and a half-mile wide with displacement on this fault varying between 500 and 1,000 feet down into the graben. The ridge above the escarpment at 3 o'clock is called Fossil Knobs (3,234 feet). It has an igneous dome buried in it that, like the one at Cuesta Blanca, has baked and hardened the surrounding limestone, making it more resistant to erosion so it stands up. The ridge is dotted with mine openings; much of the richest cinnabar ore was mined along the Long Draw near this intrusion (photograph on page 200).

The bright red mineral cinnabar was used for wall and war paint for many centuries before being found to be a source of mercury near the end of the nineteenth century. Mercury has been used in thermometers, invented by Fahrenheit in 1720, as an amalgam in dentistry, as an amalgam used in extracting gold and silver from their ores, and to manufacture mercury fulminate, used in explosives and military cartridge fuses. At Terlingua, cinnabar was found in thin stringers and occasionally larger bodies in the Cretaceous limestones that underlie most of the area. One of the early geologists who examined the area, Johannes Udden, believed that "the mercury sulfide ascended as a hot gas (from underlying igneous intrusions), was trapped in permeable limestone capped by impervious claystones in the rocks, and thereupon by cooling condensed as a solid, usually the cochineal-red mineral, cinnabar". The permeable limestone was found mainly along fractures and in breccia pipes. The impervious claystone was in the Del Rio Formation.

First recorded mention of mining in the area was in the Transactions of the American Institute of Mining Engineers in 1894 when activity was reported in the California Hill area. By 1898, a settlement had grown up around the mining activity and a post office opened up called Terlingua. The largest cinnabar mine in the United States at the time was the Almaden mine in California and California Hill was named for the many California prospectors who worked there. The Norman brothers from Marfa opened the Marfa and Mariposa Mining Company in 1899, also on California Hill. By spring 1900, two other mining operations had started up, and a mining boom was under way.

Howard Perry, a Chicago businessman, gained title to land at Long Draw Graben through nonpayment of a debt. When he received more than one offer for his land, he sent an agent to investigate, and found that it bordered some productive cinnabar properties. He decided to enter the business and formed the Chisos Mining Company in 1903. It very quickly became the dominant mine in the area, thanks to rich ore and Perry's capital and business expertise. Cinnabar was mined along the contact between Santa Elena Limestone and Del Rio Formation claystone, from calcite veins in the Boquillas and Buda Formations and from a breccia pipe. The 75-foot diameter breccia pipe was found underground in mine workings at a depth of 550 feet and was mined from there to a total depth of 840 feet. It provided the biggest and most valuable ore body in the area.

Scattered pieces of abandoned mining equipment and purplish or blue gray waste tips can be seen along the escarpment at 3 o'clock. The ones on the right are from the Chisos Mine, those on the left from the Rainbow Mine. The latter began operating in 1916, during an upsurge in demand fueled by the First World War. After a long struggle, rife with chicanery, it was taken over by Perry in 1938. Kenneth Ragsdale tells the story in his book about Terlingua and the Chisos Mine, *Quicksilver: Terlingua and the Chisos Mining Company.*

Mercury prices slumped when the First World War ended in 1918. The Chisos Mine experienced a slow decline through the 1920s and the Depression years of the 1930s, never regaining its wartime prosperity. The mine finally ran out of ore in 1942 and filed for bankruptcy. A company owned by the Brown brothers of Houston, founders of Brown and Root, bought it and spent heavily on exploration but failed to find more ore, and the mine never reopened. The Study Butte mine operated sporadically throughout the century before closing in 1946. It reopened briefly in 1970 but closed finally in 1972. The Fresno Mine, 7 miles west of Terlingua, and the 248 Mine, 2 miles east, both opened in 1940, when the onset of the Second World War created another flurry of activity. The former continued in business until 1972 and was the last mine to close.

Terlingua was a ghost town until tourism brought new life to the area in the late 1960s. It became famous for its annual chili cook-off and in 1967 was christened the "Chili Capitol of the World" by the Chili Appreciation Society. The old company store reopened as a gift and art shop, river float trips are scheduled in the former cantina and a dinner theater occupies the former motion picture theater. The combined Study Butte-Terlingua population in the 2000 census was 267.

A quarter-mile beyond the fault escarpment, a flood gauge at roadside marks Long Draw. The road traverses the graben diagonally for about 2 miles, crossing the draw two more times. The southwest boundary fault of Long Draw Graben runs along the base of Reed Plateau, the mesa on the left. It has a displacement of 1,600 feet down towards the road. Reed Plateau is an extension of the Terlingua Uplift. The Terlingua Monocline runs along its southern flank. Light colored Buda and Del Rio sedimentary rocks crop out on the escarpment with steeply dipping thick dark beds of Santa Elena limestone below.

On the other side of the graben, the road climbs 270 feet up Thirty-eight Hill, the southwestern boundary fault scarp. This fault's displacement is about 2,000 feet here. Santa Elena, Del Rio and Buda limestones are on the left, Boquillas flaggy limestone in the graben floor on the right. At the top of the hill, the Villa de la Mina exit on the right leads to the old Little Thirty-Eight Mine, where ore was mined during World War I.

Along the Terlingua Monocline

A half-mile beyond the Villa de la Mina exit, the road descends 180 feet through a Santa Elena limestone roadcut. The limestone cliffs on both sides of the road dip steeply down the Terlingua Monocline. Dips along the monocline range from 20 to 75 degrees south and strata are displaced down into the Castolon Graben on the left from 1,000 to 1,500 feet. Once down the monocline, the road continues to Lajitas on Boquillas flagstones preserved in the Castolon Graben.

Well Creek Draw crosses the road at the flood gauge. On the right, a narrow downthrown block, the Well Creek Graben, runs 3 miles northwest along the left flank of Clay Mountain (3,502 feet) at 3 o'clock. Another small graben is on the right flank of Clay Mountain. At 2 o'clock, California Hill (3,328 feet) rises above the ridge known as Sierra de Cal (3,022 feet). It has an unbedded and resistant cap of Buda limestone over Del Rio claystones, interbedded flaggy limestone and friable sandstone (photograph on page 201). Sharp cliffs face the road. Buda flatirons dip down Sierra de Cal for the next mile. The diagram on the next page shows several of these flatirons seen from Well Creek.

Croesus Canyon is at 3:30 o'clock from the Lone Star Ranch entrance, the site of a very narrow graben in Santa Elena Limestone. Tres Cuevas Mountain (3,651 feet) on its right is an anticline cresting behind the Terlingua Monocline. The name, in Spanish Three Caves, refers to three

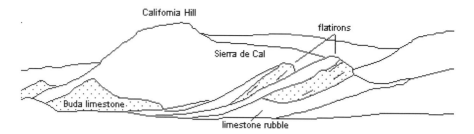

Flatirons of Buda limestone dip down the Terlingua Monocline on Sierra de Cal ((photograph on page 201)

mine openings on its northwestern face. One was that of the Lone Star Mine, which the Texas Mercury Mining Company reopened in 1970, but shut down the next year. The old road to the Lone Star Mine goes over the left flank of Tres Cuevas Mountain. Black Mesa (4,285 feet), just to the right of Tres Cuevas Mountain up Croesus Canyon, is a columnar jointed rhyolite laccolith, 34 million years old. The laccolith has domed and broken through the Cretaceous strata above it. The low yellow ridge of Boquillas limestone at 2 o'clock is called Amarilla Mountain (3,013 feet).

Lajitas Mesa dominates the skyline at 1:30 o'clock. To its right the flat-topped Contrabando Mountain (3,214 feet) is a rhyolite intrusion (*Contrabando* means contraband or smuggling in Spanish). The Terlingua Monocline turns north into the Fresno Monocline just to the right of Contrabando Mountain. Its displacement at the turn is about 800 feet to the left, diminishing to 500 feet near the Solitario.

Mesa de Anguila

The beautiful cliffs of Mesa de Anguila are on the left, their strata dipping at about 10 degrees to the west. The mesa (3,883 feet) forms the western edge of the Sunken Block, the huge graben encompassing most of the National Park (see map on page 98). The mesa runs eleven miles southeast to the Rio Grande at Santa Elena Canyon. It then becomes Sierra Ponce in Mexico. Its caprock is Santa Elena Limestone. Behind it in Mexico, the tall lava-capped mesas of Sierra del Mulato (5,427 feet) are on the skyline. Sierra Aguja is the sharp peak at 9 o'clock.

At Santa Elena Canyon, the Terlingua Fault runs along the escarpment base with a displacement of 2,900 feet to the northeast. Towards Lajitas it branches into a series of parallel faults across a 5-mile wide zone (see geological map on page 160). A mile beyond the Lone Star ranch exit, the road turns north over a low ridge just before a dry wash in line with the main branch of the fault. Looking back at 6 o'clock, the fault runs along a

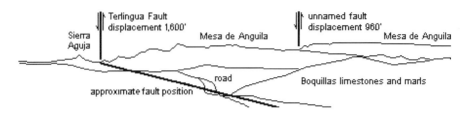

The view looking back from the road turn 3.4 miles east of Lajitas

line of low hills between the road and the northwestern tip of a fault block in the Mesa de Anguila, as shown in the diagram above. Near the tip, the fault displacement is 1,600 feet to the left. Still looking back, another fault comes towards you a mile and half to the right, this one displacing strata about 960 feet down to the left. Its fault scarp continues northwest to Lajitas. Note the fold on the skyline where beds dip down into the Rio Grande valley. The black rock at 9 o'clock is part of a widespread basalt sill dated at 34.7 Ma.

Lajitas

The road continues through rolling Boquillas limestone hills to the Barton Warnock Environmental Educational Center on the left just before Lajitas. Rainfall is sparse in this area, averaging 8.9 inches per year, only enough for a few shrubs to grow on the sandy, pebbly soil and the limestone residue. The center, part of the Big Bend Ranch State Park, has an excellent botanical garden and bookstore.

Lajitas Resort (2,364 feet) is on a bluff overlooking the Rio Grande at the San Carlos ford of the old Comanche Trail. The name *Lajitas* is Spanish for little flat rocks referring to the Boquillas flagstones. Lajitas was made a port of entry into the United States in 1900 when traffic with Mexico increased because of mining activity in Terlingua, Coahuila and Chihuahua. Farming along the narrow flood plain of the river served to bring in more families, and by 1912, the town had a store, a saloon, a school with fifty pupils, and a customhouse. The crossing, a smooth rock bottom across the river, was the best between Del Rio and El Paso.

By 1949, with the closing of the Terlingua mines, the population had dwindled to four and so it remained until Houston entrepreneur Walter M. Mischer bought part of the area in 1977. He began development and restoration of the settlement and by 2000, when it was sold to Austin

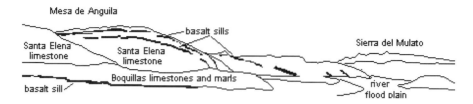

The northern tip of Mesa de Anguila from Comanche Mesa just east of Lajitas

businessman Stephen Smith, Lajitas was a resort town with seventy-five residents and fifteen businesses. The old church had been restored, and there was a hotel, a restaurant, a 9-hole golf course, a swimming pool, a RV park, and an airstrip. The old trading post remained open. Mr. Smith has added 9 holes to the golf course, a restaurant, an equestrian center and various other amenities, and has opened up substantial acreage for residential development.

The Lajitas setting is arresting. South of Highway 170, the emerald green golf course on the river flood plain is in striking contrast to the bare Boquillas mesas and mounds above it. Behind the latter, the northern tip of Mesa de Anguila dips steeply 850 feet into the flood plain on the west (photograph on page 201). The diagram above is drawn from a photograph taken from Comanche Mesa just east of the resort. Basalt sills in the Santa Elena limestones parallel to the bedding emphasize the structure, which may be a monocline. If so, its axis would be roughly north-south in line with the Fresno Monocline to the north.

North of FM 170, Lajitas Mesa rises 1,300 feet above the town (photograph on page 202). It and its twin, South Lajitas Mesa (3,069 feet), are blocks of Chisos Formation lavas and tuffaceous sedimentary rocks resting on Pen Formation claystones. Both are capped by Tule Mountain trachyte followed by more Chisos pink and white tuffs. One of the best views of both mesas is from the valley of Comanche Creek just west of Lajitas. The drawing of Lajitas Mesa opposite is from a photograph taken from there. In this view, you see the full extent of the trachyte cap. In places, a pinkish trachyte rubble lies just below the caprock. A thin bed of Bee Mountain basalt crops out on the left of the mesa. A thick bed of black Alamo Creek basalt crops out on the right. Below it, a thin conglomerate bed forms the base of the Tertiary strata and is underlain by marine calcareous claystones of the Cretaceous Pen Formation. Aguja and Javelina Formation strata are missing here.

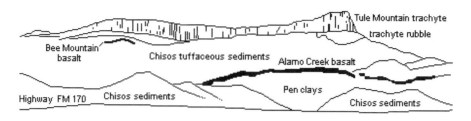

Lajitas Mesa from the valley of the arroyo west of Lajitas

Big Bend Ranch State Park

Big Bend Ranch State Park, the largest state park in Texas, was opened to the public in 1991. It comprises 280,280 acres north and west of Lajitas. Visitor centers are at Lajitas and at Fort Leaton, near Presidio. Among the park's geological attractions is a volcanic crater in the Bofecillos Mountains and The Solitario on its eastern boundary. Facilities include picnic tables at Madera Canyon, rafting and canoeing along Colorado Canyon, several trails, and an unimproved primitive campground. The area has been declared an international biosphere reserve by the federal government. It is home to eleven endangered species of plants and animals and ninety major archeological sites. Almost 400 species of birds either live in or migrate to the area.

From Lajitas, you can either continue on FM 170 to Presidio, 50 miles west, and thence to Alpine, a total of 135 miles, or return to Study Butte and travel to Alpine via Highway 118, a total of 96 miles. The next chapter includes a description of the Study Butte – Alpine section.

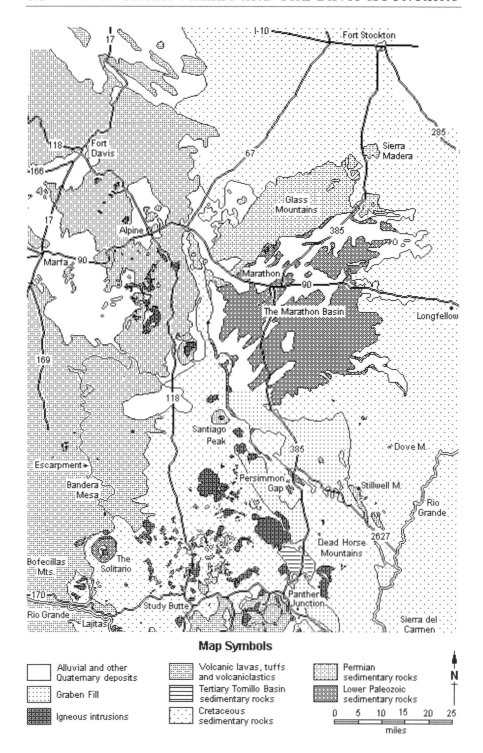

Map Symbols

☐	Alluvial and other Quaternary deposits
▦	Graben Fill
▓	Igneous intrusions
▒	Volcanic lavas, tuffs and volcaniclastics
≡	Tertiary Tomillo Basin sedimentary rocks
⬚	Cretaceous sedimentary rocks
▒	Permian sedimentary rocks
▓	Lower Paleozoic sedimentary rocks

N

0   5   10   15   20   25
miles

Geology: Green Valley and the southern Davis Mountains

IV Green Valley and the Davis Mountains

This, the final chapter describes the area from Study Butte to Fort Stockton. The first section takes in Highway 118 from Study Butte to Mitre Peak, just north of Alpine. This stretch of country includes the prolific intrusions north of Study Butte, the Green Valley plain and the rough volcanic terrain of the southern Davis Mountains. The next section examines Paisano Volcano exposures along Highway 90 west of Alpine, a fascinating close-up view of a caldera's internal structure. The final section describes the terrain along Highway 67 from Alpine to Interstate 10 near Fort Stockton, beginning in the Davis Mountains, traveling through Stockton Plateau plains and mesas and ending in the Great Plains at Interstate 10. The chapter begins by recounting the geological history of the area and explaining the structures through cross sections and maps.

Green Valley and the Southern Davis Mountains Volcanic Field

As in the rest of the Big Bend, the Cretaceous ocean covered Green Valley and the Davis Mountains until it withdrew at 75 Ma. It left behind a succession of mainly limestone strata, thick in the south and thinning to the north. After a long interval of erosion, volcanic activity began at about 47 Ma and lasted until 27 Ma. During these twenty million years, volcanoes erupted first in Mexico and then in the Chinati, Davis and Bofecillos volcanic centers and blanketed the area with volcanic ash and lava flows. The volcanic blanket merged with those produced by the Chisos and Christmas Mountain centers to the east and south. As the volcanism waned, Basin and Range faulting began but with much less impact than down by the river and only a few shallow grabens have developed. Much of the volcanic blanket has been eroded in the past 25 million years along with considerable amounts of the younger Cretaceous strata.

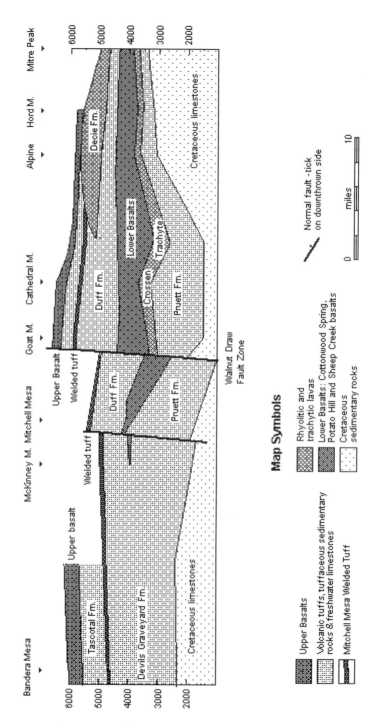

Section across volcanic strata from McKinney Mountain to Mitre Peak. Vertical scale is about 10 times the horizontal scale.

The western half of Green Valley is underlain by stream-borne strata of the Devil's Graveyard Formation, 47 to 32 Ma in age, resting on Boquillas and Aguja beds. The Devil's Graveyard strata are 1,500 feet thick along Bandera Mesa escarpment, consisting of 250 to 300 feet of limestone conglomerate at base, followed by a succession of floodplain, swamp and lake mudstones, and braided stream conglomerate and sandstone deposits. Fossilized crocodiles, sharks and large trees show that the climate was warm and humid. The lower conglomerates contain only a few fragments (or clasts, to use the geological term) of volcanic origin but the proportion rises steadily up the succession. Initial volcanic material probably came from Mexico as no volcanoes were active in Texas at 47 Ma, but by the end of deposition the nearby Chinati volcanic center was active and supplied volcanic ash to the upper strata.

McKinney Mountain, 17 miles north of Bandera Mesa, is at the southern end of the Davis Mountains volcanic field. This is the largest of the Trans-Pecos volcanic fields, measuring about 80 miles north to south and 45 miles east to west. It developed over the million and a half years from 36.8 to 35.3 Ma, in six episodes at roughly 300,000-year intervals. Only the southern part of the field is described in this chapter, the 33 miles from McKinney Mountain to Mitre Peak. The cross-section opposite is from Bandera Mesa to Mitre Peak along Longitude 103 degrees 45 minutes. The vertical scale is about 10 times the horizontal scale, so angles within the diagram are exaggerated, but horizontal and vertical relationships are accurate. Lavas in the Davis Mountains fall into two groups, as shown in the diagram on page 21. One group is in the trachybasalt area of the diagram, with slightly higher alkali content than true basalt, and the other is in the trachyte-rhyolite area.

Stream- and river-borne sedimentary rocks similar to those in the Devil's Graveyard Formation underlie lava beds throughout the entire field. They are called the Pruett Formation between McKinney Mountain and Mitre Peak, and the Huelster Formation further north. They have not been dated but predate the oldest lavas, which erupted at 36.8 Ma. The oldest lavas crop out in the Sierra Vieja west of Marfa, where they are called the Bracks Rhyolite, and along the eastern Davis Mountains from McKinney Mountain to Interstate 10, where they are called the Crossen Member of the Pruett Formation and the Star Mountain Rhyolite. The volume of this eruption, if these lavas were continuous under the Davis Mountains, would have been 240 cubic miles spread over 5,000 square miles, an enormous amount for rhyolite. The Crossen member consists of at least two flows that probably came from fissures. The lava is reddish brown on weathered surfaces, breaks with a conchoidal fracture, and is very erosion-resistant, capping mesas and hills over a wide area.

Period Name	Age m.y.	Formation	Description
Oligocene	37-24	Upper Basalt	Scattered basalt and similar lavas occurring west of the Del Norte-Santiago Mountains; most prominently on Tascotal Mesa where multiple flows of trachytic porphyry, basalt, and trachyandesite porphyry are 937 ft. thick; age of upper Rawls about 23 m.y., middle Rawls 26 m.y.
		Tascotal	Sandy rhyolitic tuff, coarse-grained sandstone, and pebble conglomerate of mafic lavas and fine-grained syenite; light gray to yellow; up to 462 feet thick at east end of Cathedral Mountain, thins northward.
		Mitchell Mesa	Cliff-forming ash flow; weathers dark reddish gray to black; thickness up to 150 ft.; age 31.5 ± 0.7 m.y.
		Duff	Rhyolitic tuff with lenticular beds of sandstone, breccia and conglomerate, and thin basaltic lavas flows; up to 1,500 ft. thick; age about 37-35 m.y.; interfingers with Decie strata around Cathedral Mountain. Combined with the lower Pruett Formation south of McKinney Mountain in the Devil's Graveyard Formation.
		Decie	Rhyolite, quartz trachyte and trachyte lavas and tuffs erupted from Paisano Volcano west of Alpine; total thickness up to 3,000 ft.; age 36.3 m.y. Five members identified:
			McIntyre Lava Member: Quartz trachyte, trachyte, some rhyolite, minor agglomeratic tuff, conglomerate, and ash-flow tuff, reddish gray, weathers dark brown; thickness up to 1,100 ft.
			McIntyre Tuff Member: Agglomeratic tuff and several small ash-flow sheets with millimeter-sized alkali feldspar phenocrysts, pink to pinkish gray; 0-300 ft. thick.
			Morrow Lava Member: Quartz trachyte, slightly porphyritic in places, dark gray, weathers dark brown, platy fracture; thickness up to 750 ft.
			Morrow Tuff Member: Yellow agglomeratic tuff inter-layered with two minor quartz trachyte ash-flow sheets, weathers orange to red brown; up to 300 ft. thick.
			Paisano Rhyolite Member: Flows, domes and minor plugs of rhyolite with minor volcanic breccia, bedded tuff and poorly welded ash-flow tuff; thickness up to 600 ft.
		Cottonwood Spring Basalt	Mafic flows; upper part of flows vesicular, amygdaloidal, reddish gray to reddish brown; middle part massive, grayish black to dark greenish black; lower part commonly flow breccia; thickness up to 330 ft.
		Pruett	Mostly tuff, some tuffaceous sandstone, conglomerate breccia, and tuffaceous non-marine limestone; tuff, grayish white, bluish gray, greenish gray, brownish gray, brown, pink and red, erodes to low rounded hills; thickness up to 800 ft.; age at base in south about 46.5 m.y., in north 38 m.y. The following members occur within the formation between the O2 Ranch and Alpine:
			Potato Hill Andesite: In upper Pruett, plagioclase phenocrysts in fine-grained reddish-brown or coarse-grained grayish-brown groundmass; upper half flow breccia, lower half massive, vesicular; thickness about 20-40 ft.; found from Kokernot Mesa to Alpine.

Period Name	Age m.y.	Formation	Description
			Sheep Canyon Basalt: In mid-Pruett, at least 4 flows, fine to medium grained, dark greenish black; up to 235 ft. thick; found from Kokernot Mesa to Alpine.
			Crossen Member: Massive, porphyritic quartz trachyte and rhyolite, stubby feldspar phenocrysts in fine- to medium-grained, grayish- to reddish-brown groundmass, hard, brittle; weathers to rusty brown, pitted surface; thickness up to 265 ft.; age about 37 m.y.; found from Kokernot Mesa to Musquiz Canyon.
Upper Cretaceous	98-66	Aguja	Claystone, green and gray, with thin lignite and coal beds interbedded with light-brown to white sandstones, grading from marine claystone in lower part to continental claystones and sandstones in upper part; 600 ft. thick at maximum.
		Pen	Mostly claystone; upper part sandy; middle part, yellow scattered sandy beds; lower 50 ft. calcareous claystone with inch-thick chalk beds, light bluish gray, weathers yellow to yellowish gray; marine fossils throughout; 220-700 ft. thick.
		Boquillas	Clayey, flaggy limestone and chalk, separated by thin marl layers; about 700 ft. thick.
Lower Cretaceous	144-98	Buda Limestone	Limestone, grayish white; 60-70 ft. thick.
		Del Rio Clay	Mostly claystone, some interbedded limestone and sandstone; claystone, soft, bluish to greenish gray, weathers yellow to light brown; 60-120 ft. thick.
		Santa Elena Limestone	Gray to brownish gray limestone, nodular in upper 40 ft.; about 130 ft. thick.

Strata in Green Valley and the Davis Mountains

The Crossen lavas were followed after a short pause by a series of basaltic lava flows, collectively called in this chapter Lower Basalt, described in detail in the table above. Layers of weathered lava, volcaniclastic beds or freshwater limestone usually separate individual flows from each other.

A further accumulation of volcaniclastic beds followed the Duff Formation, and its equivalent, the upper Devil's Graveyard Formation. In places it is composed of brilliant white tuffaceous sandstone, striking compared to the other rather drab volcaniclastics and lavas. It crops out on escarpment slopes below caprock, on Mitchell Mesa and Boat Mountain, for example.

The next lavas to appear are those of the Decie Formation, produced by the Paisano shield volcano west of Alpine, and contemporaneously with the upper Duff volcaniclastics. They dominate the landscape west of Alpine.

After a hiatus of nearly four million years, the Mitchell Mesa welded tuff erupted from the Chinati Mountain volcanic center, 50 miles west of Highway 118, at about 32 Ma. It buried 6,000 square miles of Presidio and western Brewster Counties and much of Chihuahua State in Mexico under a blanket of white-hot ash between 6 and 300 feet thick. It would have killed every living thing in its path. A welded tuff is created when ash made buoyant by hot gas begins to flow as a fluid. It can travel great distances down slopes and often up quite steep slopes. When it settles, it welds together by the combined action of the heat retained by particles, the weight of overlying material, and hot gases. A welded tuff can be as hard and resistant to erosion as lava, and is often difficult to distinguish from lava in outcrop. The Mitchell Mesa welded tuff is very hard and durable and forms the caprock on cliffs from Bandera Mesa to Mitchell Mesa. The cliffs along the west of Green Valley are up to 1,000 feet high above the low ground along Terlingua Creek. Cliffs along the north of Green Valley are as high as 700 feet.

Deposition of the welded tuff was followed by a period of sedimentation, when volcanic rocks from the Chinati volcanic center were eroded and redeposited as the Tascotal Formation, which is found along the western edge of Green Valley and on Goat and Cathedral Mountains near Alpine. Volcanic activity ended with the eruption of Upper Basalt, which is found over a wide area west of Bandera Mesa, and around Marfa, but otherwise only crops out as scattered remnants on hill tops. The Rawls Formation lavas on Tascotal Mesa came from the Bofecillos volcanic center just west of Bandera Mesa. Seven flows were erupted about 27 Ma; a final flow is dated at 22 Ma. They appear just above Bandera Mesa on Tascotal Mesa and capping the Horseshoe Mountains north of Bandera Mesa but otherwise are not seen in Green Valley. None of the other Upper Basalt occurrences have been dated.

The Christmas Mountains Intrusions

Highway 118 threads its way between an abundance of igneous intrusions for its first 15 miles north of Study Butte. Many rise in steep rocky crags 700 to 1,500 feet high. Most are rhyolite or trachyte or, intermediate between the two, quartz trachyte. Rhyolites and trachytes consist mainly of quartz and feldspar, both light-colored minerals, and fresh surfaces are light gray or occasionally a darker gray. Weathered surfaces are typically dark red or orange red from iron oxide staining.

The intrusions are quite small, generally a mile or less in diameter, and can be thought of as small blobs rising up from the magma reservoir below, and solidifying before they reach the surface. They are fine-grained, indicating that they were intruded at no great depth; shallow intrusions cool more rapidly so their crystals are smaller. Some of the narrower ones may have been feeders for lava flows higher in the succession. The intrusions are grouped around the Christmas Mountains. The Christmas Mountains have a long history of igneous activity, beginning at 47 Ma, when a gabbro laccolith was intruded west of Little Christmas Mountain. Volcanic eruptions occurred on top of the mountains at about 45 Ma, and a rhyolite laccolith is believed to have formed a dome in the mountains at 42 Ma. Most intrusions along Highway 118 fall in the age range 44-40 Ma and are very similar in composition to the local lavas. The activity all points to a long-lived pool of molten rock under the mountains that was the source of the volcanic lavas and tuffs and the intrusions.

The Sunken Block

The Sunken Block is the name given to the large graben that crosses the Rio Grande at the Big Bend and continues northwest for at least 30 miles (see map on page 98). Its southwest boundary disappears into volcanic rocks of the Bofecillos Mountains north of Lajitas. Its northeast boundary becomes indistinct around Persimmon Gap although vestiges continue intermittently as far as the Walnut Draw and Santa Fe Faults. Both of the latter disappear into alluvium near Marfa.

Study Butte is in the Cigar Mountain Graben of the Sunken Block. Around it, Cretaceous Pen Formation claystones have been preserved in the low-lying graben and crop out in badlands. The graben, a northern extension of the Castolon Graben, is bordered on the east by faulting along the Christmas Mountains and on the west by the Yellow Hill Fault (see page 162). The Christmas Mountains faulting connects to the Tascotal Mesa Fault through a fault zone that crosses Highway 118 about 10½ miles north of Study Butte and displaces strata 650 feet up to the north. Beginning at about 20 miles of Study Butte, a series of northwest-southeast faults further raise strata out of the Sunken Block for the next 12 miles so that, at the Chalk Draw Fault, 33 miles north of Study Butte, strata are 2,125 feet above their level at Study Butte. The land surface is 1,400 feet higher at Chalk Draw Fault than at Study Butte and mirrors the structure.

Terlingua Creek

Terlingua Creek, the main drainage outlet for western Brewster County, parallels Highway 118 from the Chalk Draw Fault to Study Butte. It rises in Cartwright Mesa west of Green Valley and flows in a shallow channel through Green Valley to Hen Egg Mountain, descending at 30 feet per mile. There the creek enters a graben a half-mile wide and 4 miles long with as much as 1,000 feet displacement. The channel deepens to 150 feet, and more in places, down to the Rio Grande and the gradient increases to 50 feet per mile.

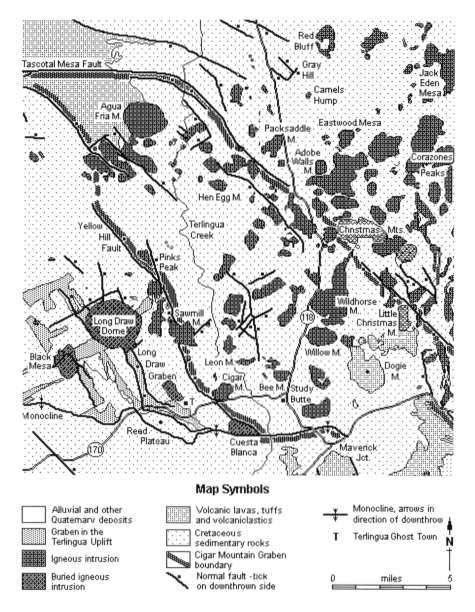

Map Symbols

☐	Alluvial and other Quaternary deposits
▨	Graben in the Terlingua Uplift
■	Igneous intrusion
▨	Buried igneous intrusion

▨	Volcanic lavas, tuffs and volcaniclastics
⬚	Cretaceous sedimentary rocks
◥	Cigar Mountain Graben boundary
⤙	Normal fault - tick on downthrown side

Monocline, arrows in direction of downthrow

T   Terlingua Ghost Town

0   miles   5

N

Geology: Study Butte to Gray Hill along Highway 118

Highway 118 Study Butte – Mitre Peak

89 miles

The Study Butte – Mitre Peak section of Highway 118 travels through an enormous variety of scenery, structure and geology. It begins in the Castolon Graben, 2,600 feet above sea level, among badlands studded with igneous intrusions. Climbing out of the graben through spectacular desert scenery intrusions dominate both sides of the road for the first 13 miles. Nowhere in Texas, and perhaps in the United States, are there so many intrusions on display. It next parallels the beautiful Green Valley for 29 miles at around 4,000 feet elevation, between escarpments and mesas of on the west and the Santiago Mountains. Then Highway 118 enters the southern Davis Mountains volcanic field and rises for 27 miles in valleys through volcanic terrain and a series of magnificent intrusive mountains to the 5,400-feet high divide between the Pecos River and Rio Grande drainage systems. The final 20 miles descends through further intrusives and volcanic cliffs into the Alpine basin and ends at Mitre Peak, 10 miles north of Alpine.

Mileages are measured from the junction of Highway 118 and FM 170 in Study Butte. Strata along the route are described in the table on pages 176-177.

Climbing out of the Sunken Block

At Study Butte, soft Pen Formation claystones, often purplish or yellowish gray in color, have eroded into irregular mounds and pedestals looking rather like mine waste heaps. It is wild desert country with little vegetation. Bee Mountain (3,452 feet) is on the left one mile north of town, a reddish, craggy trachyte dome rising above the road in sheer cliffs up to 850 feet high. The fresh rock surface as exposed in a roadcut is a light greenish gray. Two hundred yards along the roadcut, Pen limestone crops out at road level below the intrusion. The contact may be the base of the intrusion, or more likely, a limestone block that has been caught up in it. Indian Head Mountain (3,065 feet), a set of low ragged hills with reddish cliffs, is on the right about two miles east of the road, a trachyte sill-like intrusion.

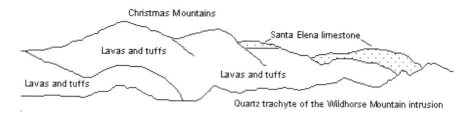

The Christmas Mountains from Mile 5.7 north of Study Butte

The Pen Formation badlands continue below the road on the left for the first three miles on leaving Study Butte while on the right, gypsum crystals in the overlying Aguja Formation glitter in the sunlight. These Aguja strata were deposited in heavily forested coastal swamps and contain lignite beds in places, one of which, 6 miles north of Study Butte, was mined by the Chisos Mining Company. To recover mercury from cinnabar, the mineral was heated to 360° F. in furnaces to release mercury vapor, which was captured in condensers. At first, local trees were used in the furnaces but the supply was rapidly used up and the Terlingua area became almost completely treeless. Costly wood had to be imported from as far away as Alpine until exploitable lignite was found. The lignite was used to make producer gas, a combustible mixture of carbon monoxide, hydrogen, carbon dioxide, methane, and nitrogen, for the furnaces by blowing steam and air through red-hot lignite.

Two miles north of town, Little Christmas Mountain is at 2:30 o'clock, 6 miles away, an eroded stack of trachyte and rhyolite lavas and ash flow tuffs which had erupted from vents on the Christmas Mountains (see page 137). The two small peaks to its left with orange and cream tuff cropping out on their flanks are most likely from the same source (photograph on page 203).

Willow Mountain (3,830 feet), a reddish brown quartz trachyte laccolith, 40 million years old, looms above the road 2½ miles north of Study Butte. Its south face provides the most spectacular display in the Big Bend region. Closely spaced, nearly vertical columns run down the cliffs from top to bottom. Fallen columns litter the ground below (photograph on page 202). Stands of native desert willows grow around Willow Spring at the base of the mountain on the south and it was probably named for them. Across the valley at 9 o'clock from Willow Mountain, an eroded laccolith caps Pen limestone (photograph on page 203). It forms a continuous ragged ridge for a little more than two miles above the road on the left.

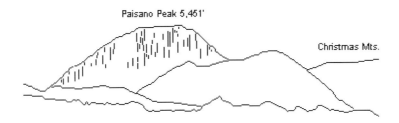

Paisano Peak is a trapdoor laccolith. The steep jointed face of the intrusion faces Highway 118 8 miles north of Study Butte.

Wildhorse Mountain (3,838 feet) rises 750 feet above the road on the right 2 miles ahead, a nearly circular quartz trachyte stock, 1½ miles in diameter, 42 million years old. A thick sill extends over 2 miles from its northeast side, giving the intrusion a strange saxophone-like shape. A further mile ahead, 5 miles from Study Butte, light greenish gray fresh rhyolite is exposed in a roadcut on the right.

Seven miles from Study Butte, the road crosses a bridge over Dark Creek Canyon. The Christmas Mountains (5,728 feet) stand 2,500 feet above the road at 3 o'clock, a magnificent, craggy, eroded dome. Volcanic breccia, produced by two small calderas on the dome, caps the highest peaks. From the road you can see the light-colored beds of Santa Elena Limestone dipping off the dome on the right. They have been elevated as much as 5,000 feet above their normal position, probably by an unexposed intrusion. A fault escarpment 1,200 feet high faces the road. The fault most likely developed during the doming but was reactivated during Basin and Range extension and now forms the western boundary of the Cigar Mountain Graben. It dies out to the northwest into a complex fault zone which crosses Highway 118 4 miles ahead and connects to the Tascotal Mesa Fault.

Paisano Peak (5,451 feet), not to be confused with the Paisano Peak west of Alpine, is the sharp pointed hill at 2 o'clock, a rhyolite trapdoor laccolith, 45 million years old. The 1,200-feet escarpment facing the road is the trapdoor opening. On the opposite side, remnants of Buda and Del Rio strata slope away from the summit (see Adobe Walls diagram on the following page). Fluorspar was mined on the west side of the peak from 1971 to 1980. The main source of the element fluorine, fluorspar is found in limestone near contacts with rhyolite intrusions in the Christmas Mountains and in Mexico.

Just ahead, the road cuts through the base of an unnamed quartz trachyte intrusion (4,234 feet) rising 900 feet above on the right, 43 million

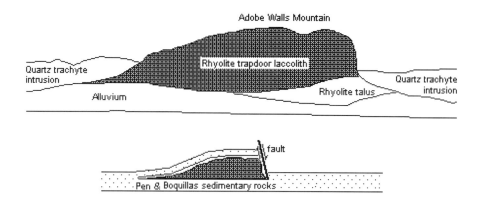

Adobe Walls Mountain is a good example of a trapdoor laccolith. In this type of intrusion, overlying strata are faulted up at one end. The intrusion has a steep escarpment at the faulted end and tails away at the other end.

years old. Its sheer rock face is reddish brown and jointed but the fresh rock surfaces are dark gray in the roadcut.

Nine miles north of Study Butte, the quartz trachyte Luna Vista Sill crosses the road and is exposed in a roadcut. Bedded Pen Formation claystone crops out below the sill, baked and hardened by the heat of the intrusion (photograph on page 203). A short distance ahead, two further roadcuts go through the western edge of the Lake Ament intrusion (4,375 feet), a quartz trachyte plug which rises 700 feet above the road, 43 million years old.

North County Road, part of the old Terlingua-Alpine road, enters from the left 10½ miles north of Study Butte. For its first 4.6 miles it is a graveled county road open to the public that descends 500 feet over steep grades into the valley of Terlingua Creek. While the road provides excellent views up the valley to Hen Egg and Agua Fria Mountains, it is often washed out and needs to be navigated with care.

North County Road is at the northern edge of a belt of faulting connecting the Tascotal Mesa Fault to faulting along the Christmas Mountains. Strata have been stepped up by the faulting; the Boquillas-Pen boundary here is at 3,308 feet elevation, 750 feet higher than at Study Butte. The road passes on to flaggy limestones of the Boquillas Formation and continues on them until it enters the Davis Mountains volcanic field 30 miles ahead. Boquillas limestones are easily eroded and seldom form more than low hills. Flaggy fragments litter the roadside and show up in roadcuts, clean looking compared to muddy Pen and Aguja strata.

Hen Egg Mountain (5,002 feet) is at 8:30 o'clock, 3½ miles west of the sign for the peak. It is a rhyolite plug, 40 million years old, one of a group of four, most likely from a common underlying source. The upper 1,500 feet of the mountain is above the level that the top of the surrounding Devil's Graveyard strata would have been at the time of the intrusion and so must have broken through into the open air. Two more peaks of the group are to its immediate right.

Adobe Walls Mountain (4,510 feet), at 3 o'clock, is a fine example of a trapdoor laccolith, of which there are many occurrences in this area. In a trapdoor laccolith, a rising intrusion raises the sedimentary rocks above it as shown in the diagrams opposite. The sedimentary rocks break at some point in the periphery, creating a fault and a steep face in the intrusion below. Adobe Walls Mountain rises in a long slope from the plain below, and falls off to the south in a cliff 600 feet high. The overlying Boquillas and Pen sedimentary rocks have been eroded off the rhyolite intrusion, which is slightly older than Hen Egg Mountain, 44 million years. Below the cliff, a talus slope is littered with boulders.

A mile ahead, 13½ miles from Study Butte, the road crests a rise at 3,450 feet elevation, 1,000 feet above Study Butte. Good views extend over the moderately level terrain at right front. Santiago Peak is the flat-topped peak 20 miles ahead at 2 o'clock.

Packsaddle Mountain (4,658 feet) rises 1,200 feet above the road 1½ miles west of the sign for the mountain. It is a rhyolite plug in which the intrusion has broken through Santa Elena Limestone. Some light-colored beds of limestone remain on its flanks, particularly on the northeast side, tilted up by the intrusion. Near the road, two dikes run parallel to the road, creating iguana-like ridges (photograph on page 204).

A half-mile beyond the Packsaddle Mountain sign, the small double hill at 3 o'clock is Camels Hump (3,662 feet), a rhyolite plug intruded into Boquillas limestone. Though it was probably named for its shape, Camels Hump also lay on the route through this area of a United States Army camel expedition commanded by Lieutenant Echols in 1859. The expedition was a War Department experiment to see how camels could be used in the Southwest. The answer was that they did not work very well. Their feet were cut up by the sharp rocks so prevalent in the Big Bend. It was abandoned on the outbreak of the Civil War and the Confederate army captured the animals. Some were set loose; stray camels were sighted for several years in West Texas.

Jack Eden Mesa (3,961 feet), behind Camels Hump 8 miles away at 3 o'clock is capped by a 10-square mile sill. The Rosillos Mountains are over its right shoulder on the skyline with the Christmas Mountains at 3:30 o'clock, looking spectacularly rugged.

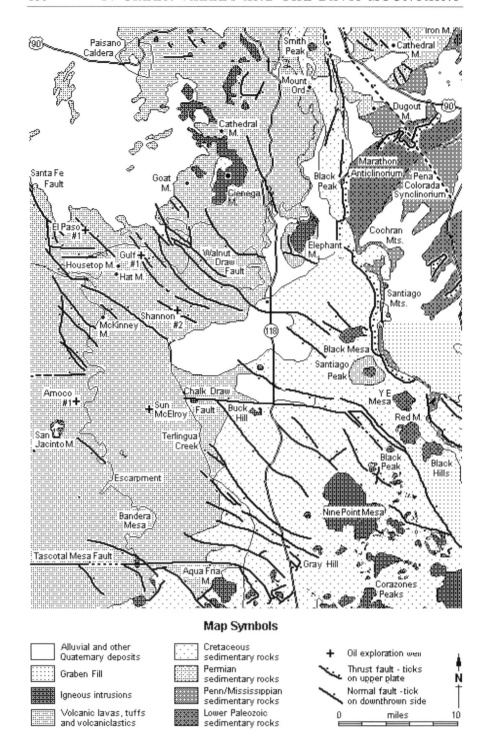

Map Symbols

Alluvial and other Quaternary deposits	Cretaceous sedimentary rocks	Oil exploration well
Graben Fill	Permian sedimentary rocks	Thrust fault - ticks on upper plate
Igneous intrusions	Penn/Mississippian sedimentary rocks	Normal fault - tick on downthrown side
Volcanic lavas, tuffs and volcaniclastics	Lower Paleozoic sedimentary rocks	0 miles 10

Geology: Gray Hill to Mount Ord along Highway 118

Small intrusions into Aguja siltstones and Pen shales have created the low brown hills on the left before and after the Terlingua Ranch Road intersection. These outliers have been protected from erosion by the hard intrusions and are the last Aguja outcrops along Highway 118.

A bentonite processing operation is on the left 25 miles north of Study Butte. Bentonite is a clay mineral used as a lubricant in drilling mud and as a binder in animal feed pellets. Occurring in Pruett volcaniclastics as irregular lenses near the base of the formation, the weathered product of volcanic ash, it is quarried in the low-lying terrain west of the road, ground into powder and bagged.

Agua Fria Mountain (4,828 feet) is 7 miles away at 8 o'clock from the Agua Fria Road intersection, 19 miles from Study Butte. It is a dissected rhyolite body 2 miles in diameter and towering 1,400 feet above the surrounding countryside. Huge, irregular columns of reddish weathered rock form cliffs around its periphery. Panther Mountain (4,331 feet) is the craggy peak to its left, a rhyolite trapdoor laccolith like Adobe Walls Mountain, surrounded by sheer cliffs 600 feet high. It retains some of its sedimentary cover. Santa Elena Limestone strata dip steeply off its southern side although they can't be seen from the road.

Red Bluff (4,018 feet) at 4 o'clock is a narrow crescent-shaped wall, rising 600 feet above the surrounding flat and 350 feet above a laccolithic intrusion behind it. It was injected into a fault created when the laccolith was intruded and uncovered by erosion. Two hills further up the draw also have intrusive cores. Behind them, slightly to their left on the skyline, are the Rosillos Mountains, an enormous rounded laccolith. The two Corazones peaks are to the right of Red Bluff. The one to the right stands alone, either a rhyolite laccolith or a stock. The other, less high and steep, is part of a trachyte intrusion.

Red Bluff is the last of the intrusions crowded together around the Christmas Mountains. From this point north, intrusions are more widely spaced until near Alpine. One of the widely spaced intrusions is Nine Point Mesa (5,502 feet), a massive presence six miles east of Agua Fria Road, 2,000 feet above Highway 118. Roughly circular, six to seven miles across, it is capped by two sills of quartz trachyte 1,000 feet thick, which form 200-ft igneous cliffs set on a pediment of Pen and Boquillas sedimentary rocks. It is among the oldest intrusions in the area, one of its sills being dated at about 46 m.y. Two deep canyons following northwest-southeast faults dissect the intrusion. The northeastern end of one of them, Cartwright Canyon, can be seen from the road 2½ miles ahead.

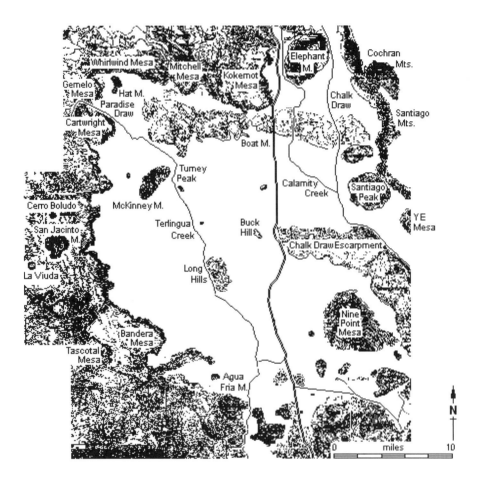

Green Valley physiography

The Cheosa Waterhole Fault crosses Highway 118 just before Agua Fria Road and another parallel to it shortly ahead, with downthrows of 250 and 200 feet respectively to the southwest. The Pen-Boquillas boundary is about 3,500 feet elevation here, 925 feet higher than at Study Butte. For the next 13 miles, strata have been broken into blocks by a series of northwest southeast faults (see map on page 186) that continue to raise strata up to the northeast out of the Sunken Block. The blocks, however, are slightly tilted to the south so that the overall displacement is less than the total of the individual fault displacements (compare to the cross section on page 106 in which a similar situation occurs).

The southern margin of Green Valley from 25 miles north of Study Butte

The O2 Ranch

Cowboy Mining Company, another bentonite operation, is on the left 6 miles ahead, 25 miles north of Study Butte. Green Valley and Terlingua Creek come into view on the other side of the buildings. About a half-mile ahead, the fence line is the southern boundary of the O2 Ranch. It runs west along Highway 118 for 19 miles. Ranch headquarters are near the foot of Turney Peak, named for one of the early owners. The ranch was established in 1892 and was for many years the largest in the Trans-Pecos. From 1905 to 1936, it averaged between 10,000 and 12,000 high-grade Hereford cattle on 250,000 to 300,000 acres in Brewster and Presidio counties. In the early 1950s, when it last changed ownership, the 264,555 acres (413 square miles) of O2 Ranch land in Brewster and Presidio counties made it the eleventh-largest ranch in Texas. It was bought then by Lykes Brothers Inc., a family-owned firm, run by the descendants of seven brothers who began in business shipping cattle to Cuba. The family now own 600,000 acres of land in Florida and Texas.

Green Valley

Agua Fria Mountain is on the southern boundary of Green Valley where the landscape changes to rolling plains with isolated igneous intrusions. Rather than a valley, Green Valley is a flat-bottomed basin created by erosion in the normal desert way. It may have begun as a valley along Terlingua Creek, but then escarpments developed and receded, leaving pediments or flats behind. The western boundary is now 10 miles west of Terlingua Creek, a beautiful volcanic escarpment, 35 miles long, from Agua Fria Mountain to the Davis Mountains at Gemelo Mesa. The northern boundary is also an escarpment, 15 miles long, from Whirlwind to Kokernot Mesas. The eastern basin boundary is less regular. It laps up against fault blocks and intrusions such as Nine Point Mesa, but where unimpeded stretches as far east as the Santiago Mountains. Terlingua Creek runs diagonally across the basin in a shallow channel, 200 feet below the road here.

The area around Green Valley has been lightly folded into a series of low amplitude synclines and anticlines, now much broken up by faulting.

One such anticline runs across the basin towards its northwest corner, and strata on its west flank are tilted to the southwest at around 5 degrees. As a result, Bandera Mesa (4,685 feet), 12 miles away at 8 o'clock, tilts away as a cuesta. Its 800-foot high escarpment faces east, capped by Mitchell Mesa welded tuff over Devil's Graveyard volcaniclastics. Behind it, Tascotal Mesa (5,152 feet) at 8:30 also tilts to the west, capped by Rawls Formation basalts from the Bofecillos Mountains volcanic center. The top of the Boquillas Formation, 4,200 feet on Santiago Peak 10 miles east of here, climbs up to 4,700 feet at roadside and then over the crest of the anticline, dips down into Green Valley under volcaniclastic rocks along Terlingua Creek where it was intersected at 3,400 feet in the Sun McElroy oil exploration well 22 miles west of the highway.

Shortly after the entrance to Cowboy Mining, the road climbs up the escarpment of the Hale Cabin Fault, one of the northwest southeast-trending faults in the Sunken Block, with a displacement of 500 feet to the southwest. It is approximately in line with Cartwright Canyon in Nine Point Mesa and you can see the fault trace in the mesa looking back from the fault scarp. Boquillas Formation strata crop out in several roadcuts coming up and at the top of the escarpment. The Boquillas here consists of 12-inch limestone beds interspersed with dark marl beds 8-10 inches thick. Marl is a mixture of clay and limestone.

Five miles ahead, 30 miles from Study Butte, a windmill and mesquite trees near the road on the right indicate water present along a fault zone. This is the last of the northwest-southeast faults of the Sunken Block. It has a displacement of 600 feet up to the northeast. The road follows the fault for 2½ miles until it curves to the right and begins descending the Chalk Draw Fault scarp. Goat Mountain is dead ahead along this straight. The block between the two faults, shown on the map on page 188 as the Chalk Draw Escarpment, is a low horst. Buck Hill (4,184 feet) stands up 250 feet above the Boquillas at 9 o'clock, a mesa capped by a quartz trachyte sill.

The Chalk Draw Fault

The Chalk Draw Fault crosses Highway 118 33 miles north of Study Butte with a displacement of 300 feet to the north, increasing to 1,500 feet opposite Persimmon Gap. To the west, it cuts the north slope of Straddlebug Mountain and is also exposed in Terlingua Creek. It then appears to change into a strike-slip fault. Indirect evidence at Plata, 28 miles west, suggests a horizontal movement of 6,000 feet in which strata north of the fault are suspected of moving to the east relative to strata on the south. This right-lateral movement, to give it its technical name, is in the same direction as in the Tascotal Mesa Fault further south. Similar movement has also been proposed for the Walnut Draw Fault ahead.

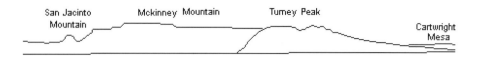

The western edge of Green Valley at McKinney Mountain (photograph on page 204)

Although the Chalk Draw Fault has modest dimensions today it is part of what has been called one of the major structural lines of the western hemisphere, running from the Chinati Mountains to Del Rio. It has been active several times in geological history. In the early Permian period, for example, the fault displaced strata 10,000 feet down to the north, according to data provided by exploration oil wells in western Green Valley. The structural map on page 98 shows several features along or near this structural line, including the intrusions Santiago Peak and the Black Hills, and the zigzag in the Santiago Mountains just south of Santiago Peak.

The parking area midway down the scarp is a good place to stop and view the wonderful panorama of the mountains to the west and north and the O2 Ranch below. Ahead in Green Valley, Boquillas and Devil's Graveyard strata form low rolling hills at most. Small intrusions and remnants of volcanic flows produce other scattered hills. Terlingua Creek lies about 6 miles west and 300 feet below the road. At 9 o'clock, Straddlebug Mountain (3,942 feet) looks like a small packsaddle in the distance on the right flank of Buck Hill. A trachyte plug, less than 1,000 feet across, is intruded into limestone which has been baked to a dark, fine-grained marble along the contacts with the intrusion. The hard marble and trachyte explain why the hill is 300 feet above its surroundings.

Behind Straddlebug Mountain, Mitchell Mesa welded tuff caps the escarpment on the skyline at the western edge of Green Valley. Scattered intrusions rise above the mesas. At 9 o'clock, the sharp spire is La Viuda (4,101 feet), a circular basalt volcanic breccia vent emplaced in Tascotal and Mitchell Mesa strata. At about 9:30 o'clock, San Jacinto Mountain (5,082 feet) stands on a mesa of sheer rock cliffs with a pediment below. Its spire is a quartz trachyte intrusion that has elevated Mitchell Mesa strata 400 feet above the surrounding mesa. Cerro Baludo (Spanish for round or bald hill) is the narrow butte, a basaltic intrusion (elevation 4,749 feet), just to the right of San Jacinto Mountain.

The massive swaybacked McKinney Mountain (5,006 feet) at 9:30 o'clock is 5 miles east of the main body of the welded tuff. Only a narrow

The northwest corner of Green Valley from Chalk Draw pullout

band of Mitchell Mesa material remains on top of the mountain but it is 150 feet thick rather than the normal 40 to 75 feet, so this extra thickness probably explains why it has survived so far in front of the main escarpment. The peak is named for W. Q. McKinney, who in 1886 built a rock house nearby. On Turney Peak (4,854 feet), just to its right, the welded tuff has been eroded off completely, leaving the underlying Duff Formation strata unprotected. Its rounded top shows that it is being eroded rapidly. Its name comes from William Turney, who founded the O2 ranch in 1888.

Cartwright Mesa (5,180 feet) is behind Turney Peak, 16 miles west of Highway 118. The Santa Fe Fault runs through Jordan Gap between it and Gemelo Mesa to its right, displacing strata at least 700 feet down to the southwest. Terlingua Creek rises in a canyon behind Cartwright Mesa and flows through Jordan Gap into Green Valley.

Two other prominent peaks on the west skyline at 10 o'clock are Hat Mountain (5,286 feet), shaped like a hat, and Housetop Mountain (5,333 feet) just to its right, both capped by Mitchell Mesa welded tuff. Whirlwind Mesa, the light-colored Mitchell Mesa, and Kokernot Mesa are to the right of Housetop Mountain. Goat and Cienega Mountains are on the skyline behind the latter two.

The Walnut Draw Fault, between Kokernot and Mitchell Mesas, down throws strata 1,100 feet to the southwest. As a result the Mitchell Mesa welded tuff capping the latter is only 400 feet higher than the Crossen trachyte capping the former, although if it were not faulted down it would be 1,600 feet above the trachyte. The beautiful white Duff tuffs on the flanks of Mitchell Mesa at 10 o'clock are 1,015 feet thick and noticeably lighter than the Pruett tuffs on Kokernot Mesa.

Looking back to the right of the road from the bottom of the hill, the Chalk Draw Fault escarpment runs down the narrow Chalk Draw valley. The cap rock on the horst above is Boquillas and Buda limestones with a brownish slope below underlain by Del Rio shales and then a 100-foot cliff of Santa Elena Limestone.

On the left, Pen Formation claystone and thin sandstone beds dip down the Terlingua Monocline near the Study Butte entrance to Big Bend National Park. On the right, Aguja claystone and sandstone are exposed in a roadcut at the base of Todd Hill, 9.5 miles west of Panther Junction.

Multicolored Javelina strata dip down the Terlingua Monocline just below the Study Butte entrance to the National Park. The purplish horizons are fossil soil layers (page 75). The Terlingua Monocline can be traced from The Solitario near Lajitas to the upper reaches of Rough Creek, where it disappears into alluvium.

Casa Grande, seen from The Window Viewpoint in the Chisos Basin, is a South Rim volcanic rhyolite dome overlying reddish-brown Wasp Spring surge deposits, pyroclastic flows and basalt, above Chisos Formation basalt and tuff (see diagram on page 146). The basal South Rim basalt is a half-inch from the bottom right. Chisos Formation gray tuffaceous sandstone crops out at bottom right.

These two photographs from The Window Viewpoint show how the Chisos Mountains Pluton becomes more jointed from Vernon Bailey Peak on the left to Pulliam Peak on the right. Weathering along joints has created columns, pinnacles, spires and buttresses on the latter, giving it a rougher profile than that of the former. Note how the pluton is pink tinged in contrast to the gray Casa Grande.

Casa Grande is framed in The Window from Mile 3 on Ross Maxwell Scenic Drive. Vernon Bailey Peak is on the left of The Window and the sharp Carter Peak on the right followed by Ward Mountain.

This photograph was taken from Mile 5.5 on Ross Maxwell Scenic Drive. A fault trace in the Burro Mesa Fault Zone runs up a gully in a face of Chisos strata 2 inches from the right margin of the photograph. Downthrow on the fault is to the right. The crest of Sierra Quemada is on the skyline at left. The figure on page 148 was drawn from this photograph.

Emory Peak, seen here from Sotol Vista Viewpoint on Ross Maxwell Scenic Drive, is the third highest mountain in Texas (7,825 feet). The high summit is a volcanic dome similar to the one at Casa Grande, and the mountain is suspected of being the site of a volcanic vent. Chisos Formation tuffs crop out on the lower slopes. The Chisos Mountains pluton tails off in the foreground.

Mule Ear Peaks, from the Mule Ear Peaks Exhibit on Ross Maxwell Scenic Drive, are the eroded remnants of two dikes intruded into Wasp Spring flow breccia overlying Bee Mountain basalt and Chisos tuffs. In Round Mountain on the right, a suspected volcanic vent, Burro Mesa rhyolite overlies Wasp Spring flow breccia. Gray Chisos Formation tuff crops out in a gully on the lower right.

Burro Mesa, photographed from the Burro Mesa Pour-off road junction on Ross Maxwell Scenic Drive, is the site of an explosive volcanic vent that created a V-shaped crater in Chisos tuffs and lavas and filled it in with pyroclastic flows and lavas. We see the crater in cross-section here with Burro Mesa rhyolite overlying the yellow Wasp Spring pyroclastic flows. Bee Mountain basalt crops out at the lower right and an intrusive plug at the lower left.

Chisos Formation tuff crops out on both sides of the road at the Cerro Castellan Exhibit on Ross Maxwell Scenic Drive. The soft white rock is composed of the mineral clinoptilolite, a zeolite.

Cerro Castellan, seen from the Desert Mountain Overlook, just west of Cottonwood Campground on Ross Maxwell Scenic Drive, is also the site of a volcanic vent, the source of the capping Burro Mesa rhyolite and the underlying Wasp Spring pyroclastic flows. A cross section from the same viewpoint is on page 154.

Just to the left of the above photograph, the Chisos Mountains make a powerful statement on the skyline from the Desert Mountain Overlook on Ross Maxwell Scenic Drive. To their right, Kit and Goat Mountains are in the intermediate distance below South Rim. A ridge capped by Ash Creek basalt is in the foreground left.

Santa Elena Canyon is best seen from the river bank on Ross Maxwell Scenic Drive. Santa Elena limestone makes up the upper third of the cliff. The ledge below is of soft Sue Peaks shale, marl and limestone, underlain by the other main cliff-forming Cretaceous limestone, the Del Carmen limestone. Marls and limestones of the Telephone Canyon Formation crop out near water level. The canyon is about 1,600 feet high here. The Terlingua Fault runs along the base of the cliffs. It displaces strata down about 2,900 feet towards the camera.

Thin-bedded Boquillas limestones and marls crop out in the cliffs along Terlingua Creek, 1½ miles west of Study Butte on FM 170. Cigar Mountain, an intrusion, is on the horizon, with Hen Egg Mountain, another intrusion, on its left flank 12 miles away.

This view of the eastern fault scarp of Long Draw is from 5 miles west of Study Butte on FM 170. Long Draw is a graben in the Terlingua Uplift. The eastern boundary fault downthrows strata between 500 and 1,000 feet into the draw. The blue material along the escarpment is waste brought up from underground workings of the Chisos Mine.

On the left, Buda limestone dips down the Terlingua Monocline at the base of 248 Hill, 8 miles west of Study Butte on FM 170. On the right, looking back from Lone Star Mine Ranch entrance 2 miles ahead, Buda limestone flatirons dip off California Hill and the Sierra de Cal ridge to its right.

This beautiful view of Lajitas Golf Course and the northern end of Mesa de Anguila is from the Candelilla Cafe terrace in Lajitas. The golf course is on the flood plain of the Rio Grande, out of sight on the right. Note how the black basalt beds in the Mesa de Anguila limestones accentuate strata dipping down into the floodplain in what may be a monocline.

Lajitas Mesa, photographed from Lajitas Equestrian Center, is a block of volcanic rocks preserved by the dark Tule Mountain trachyte on its crest. Chisos tuffs and lava flows underlie the trachyte. Several dark basalt beds can be seen in the mesa's flanks. Multicolored tuffs crop out at right near the base of the mesa.

Willow Mountain, photographed from 1 mile N of Study Butte on Highway 118, has one of the best displays of jointing seen in the Big Bend. Quartz trachyte columns up to 400 feet long run down the face. Debris litters the base of the hill. The mountain is a trapdoor laccolith; its door opens obliquely to the left. Trapdoor laccoliths are discussed on page 184.

Continuing to the right from the previous photograph, light-colored Santa Elena lime-stone dip off the Christmas Mountains on the skyline. The dome was probably created by a hidden intrusion. Little Christmas Mountain on the right is made up of a succession of lavas and tuffs, some originating in the Christmas Mountains. The orange and white small hills in front center are probably of similar origin.

A sill caps Pen badlands on the left 2 miles north of Study Butte on Highway 118. On the right, an intrusion overlying Pen strata is exposed in roadcut 5 miles north of Study Butte. Note the light bluish gray color of the intrusion on this fresh surface.

Packsaddle Mountain, 14 miles north of Study Butte on Highway 118, is domelike uplift caused by a rhyolite plug, cropping out in the brown rocks near the summit. Lighter-colored Cretaceous limestones flank the lower reaches of the plug on the left and center. The iguana-crested ridge in front is a dike standing above softer Boquillas limestones and marls.

McKinney Mountain, on the left, and Turney Peak, photographed here from 35 miles north of Study Butte on Highway 118, are volcanic outliers standing 5 miles east of the escarpment along western Green Valley. McKinney Mountain is capped by an unusually thick bed of durable Mitchell Mesa welded tuff, overlying white Duff tuffaceous volcaniclastics.

The most distinctive peak in the Alpine area, Cathedral Mountain is photographed here from Calamity Creek bridge, 56 miles north of Study Butte on Highway 118. A cross-section from this viewpoint is given on page 213. The spire on the right has been uplifted about 450 feet by faults created by an intrusion that crops out only on the lower slopes.

This view of Cathedral Mountain is from Cathedral Mountain Road, 65 miles north of Study Butte on Highway 118. It shows both the upper basalt bench, dipping to the right at 5 degrees, and the lower bench, which creates a mesa and a butte capped by Mitchell Mesa welded tuff. The white outcrops below the welded tuff are of Duff tuffaceous volcaniclastics. This view is sketched on page 215.

Highway 118, once it enters the Davis Mountains volcanic field at Elephant Mountain, has many exposures of Lower Basalt in roadcuts. In this example, 24.5 miles south of Alpine, 49 miles north of Study Butte, lava above tuff and then limestone are exposed on the right of the highway.

The Crossen member of the Pruett Formation is the most prominent lava in the Alpine area, best exposed in a series of roadcuts in Big Hill, 6 miles south of Alpine on Highway 118. On fresh surfaces, the rock is a light purple in color. In joints the rock is cream colored as in the above photograph, although this is only superficial.

One of the common landforms assumed by lava beds when eroded is the pyramid. This one, in Morrow lava 5 miles west of Alpine on Highway 90, has been called a hoodoo by some geologists. The Morrow member of the Decie Formation includes tuff in addition to the quartz trachyte lava. Small light-colored tuff outcrops can be seen near the base of the hill.

On the left, a fossil mudflow consists of a jumbled collection of volcanic pebbles are set in a groundmass of mud at 12.9 miles west of Alpine on Highway 90. On the right, a large red block of welded tuff is set in soft white tuff, also probably the result of a fossil mudflow, 10 miles west of Alpine on Highway 90. Both are in the Paisano volcano caldera.

Another example from the Paisano volcano caldera is this photograph from Mile 12.8 west of Alpine on Highway 90. It shows a blue-gray dike towards the right margin bisecting a block of red welded tuff. Large numbers of dikes were intruded after the caldera collapsed and are seen in roadcuts from the Paisano Encampment to the top of Paisano Pass.

In this photograph, taken from 13 miles west of Alpine on Highway 90, a large block of welded tuff megabreccia overlies tuff in a roadcut on the left. Megabreccia is the term used for large blocks of rock that have moved from their original location but are still in their original orientations. They are a common feature of calderas where the land surface has sagged.

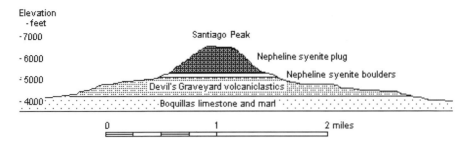

Section across Santiago Peak from the bottom of the Chalk Draw Fault scarp

Santiago Peak (6,521 feet) at 2:30 o'clock is one of the most striking landmarks in the Big Bend, rising very steeply 2,750 feet above Highway 118. The upper part is a nepheline syenite intrusion 1,250 feet thick and about ¾ mile in diameter. Boulders cover its lower boundary so it is not possible to say whether it is a plug or the remnant of a larger sill such as the ones capping Nine Point Mesa and Elephant Mountain but its shape suggests that it is a plug. The intrusion overlies 900 feet of Devil's Graveyard volcaniclastic sandstones protected by the igneous body above. Four hundred and fifty feet of Boquillas strata, also protected by the intrusion, stand up above the plain under the volcaniclastics.

The cockscomb ridge to the right of Santiago Peak is Y E Mesa (5,385 feet), a syenite sill 2 miles in diameter and about 1,400 feet thick (see diagram on page 58). The name comes from a cattle brand used locally in the early twentieth century. To its right the dome-shaped Red Mountain (4,100 feet) and the sharp Black Peak (4,800 feet) are also intrusions. The very dark Black Mesa (4,610 feet) to the left of Santiago Peak is a trachyte sill 3 miles long and 600 feet thick. Between them, a light-colored Cretaceous limestone mesa in the Santiago Mountains is on the skyline.

Butcherknife Hill (4,042 feet), the low brown hill a mile in front at 11:30 o'clock, is a small basalt intrusion in Pruett tuff and conglomerate overlying Boquillas limestone.

The Southern Davis Mountains Volcanic Field

Three miles beyond Butcherknife Hill, the road crosses Butcherknife Draw, a dry reed-filled watercourse. The butte at 10:30 o'clock is capped by basalt lava, the most southerly exposure of Davis Mountains lavas. The basalt here consists of up to nine separate lava flows, 300 feet thick at maximum. Beautiful light gray Pruett bedded tuffaceous sandstone crops out on the slopes below, especially in Boat Mountain. To its right irregular low hills, also of basalt, end in a rough bluff, typical of volcanic erosion throughout the Davis Mountains.

Boat Mountain and the basalt-capped hills to its left from the pullout at the base of the Walnut Draw Fault, 35.3 miles north of Study Butte

Forty-four miles from Study Butte, the Walnut Draw Fault zone crosses the road in a 160-foot high escarpment. It runs down Walnut Draw between Mitchell and Kokernot Mesas at about 10 o'clock and cuts diagonally across the road before disappearing into alluvium near Black Mesa. Boquillas and Buda limestones underlie the low ridges ahead on its upthrown side. Displacement is about 1,100 feet at Mitchell Mesa. It lessens to 750 feet at Highway 118 and 300 feet near Black Mesa.

Chalk Draw continues up Chalk Valley, the plain to the right of Elephant Mountain. At 2 o'clock, craggy limestone beds on the Cochran Mountains tilt to the north. The notch in the range just north of the Cochran Mountains is Del Norte Gap (Paso del Norte). The old road from Marathon to Terlingua climbed 200 feet up this pass.

The entrance to the O2 Ranch is on the left on top of the escarpment. Kokernot Mesa rises 800 feet above the road on the left ahead. Its cap rock is Crossen trachyte, 120 feet thick and jointed into columns at the top. The pinnacle on the left is separated from the main part of the caprock and looks ready to fall down the cliff. Light-colored Pruett tuffs crop out below the caprock.

From this point on, the road winds between rough, boulder-littered mesas, buttes and ridges capped by horizontal basalt flows and their eroded remains. It parallels Calamity Creek, now 2 miles to the east, for the next 11 miles, climbing slowly at 40 feet per mile. It then follows Ash Creek, a tributary of Calamity Creek, for another 11 miles to its headwaters at the divide between the Pecos and Rio Grande drainage basins, climbing at 80 feet per mile. After crossing a beautiful basin west of Mount Ord, it descends Big Hill into the Alpine basin.

The Crossen lava was produced from scattered fissures by the first volcanic episode in the Davis Mountains volcanic field about 37 million years ago as one of three similar lavas that crop out along the eastern and western margins of the field. It is missing on Elephant Mountain, where presumably it has been eroded away. It does not crop out south of the Walnut Draw Fault, just 1½ miles from Kokernot Mesa, although it was found in well cuttings south of the fault near Goat Mountain to the west.

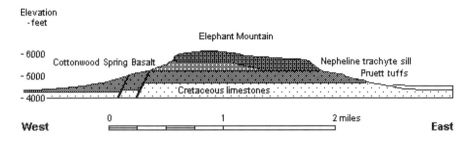

Section across Elent Mountain

Bruce Pearson concluded that the Walnut Draw Fault is a right-lateral fault, like the Tascotal Mesa Fault and perhaps the Chalk Draw Fault, in which strata to its south moved west in relation to strata to its north. Thus the area south of the fault came from the left where the Crossen had been eroded away.

Elephant Mountain (6,206 feet) dominates the immediate foreground, capped, like Black Mesa, by a nepheline trachyte sill. This enormous sill is 4 miles long, 2 miles wide, 1,200 feet thick and weighs about 3 billion tons. As the cross-section above shows, the sill is above the Cottonwood Spring basalt on the west and below it on the east. The mountain was named for its shape, which resembles an elephant's back. On the right front, Nevill Mesa is the somewhat irregular mesa on the skyline, sloping gently to the left. The sharp peak of Mount Ord is behind it on the skyline. Calamity Creek flows down an alluvium-covered flat 1½ miles wide between Elephant Mountain and the escarpment on the left. The Crossen caprock on the left of the road dips at 1 to 2 degrees to the north and gradually loses height as we go north.

Bear Canyon is at 9 o'clock from the sign for Elephant Mountain, separating Kokernot Mesa from Crossen Mesa. A fault runs up the canyon, displacing strata 115 feet down to the left. The fault extends 6 miles northwest to Goat Mountain, its displacement increasing to 350 feet west of Kokernot Mesa.

Little Cienega Mountain and Cienega Mountain can be seen through Sheep Creek Canyon, the next canyon on the left two miles ahead. Non-marine limestone is exposed on the right; the limestone formed in saline lakes that developed from time to time on the Pruett sediments. The climate at the time was quite wet and mild.

The entrance to the 23,000-acre Elephant Mountain Wildlife Management Area (WMA) is on the right. Its principal wildlife species are

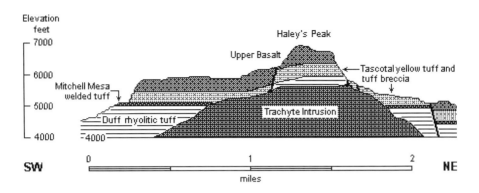

Cathedral Mountain cross-section from the bridge over Calamity Creek

javelina, pronghorn, quail, and dove. Bighorn sheep were introduced in 1987, although not native to the Trans-Pecos. The Texas Parks and Wildlife Department maintains a comprehensive web site on the Area, *www.tpwd.state.tx.us/wma/wmarea/elephant.htm.*

Limestones crop out on the flanks of the hill on the left. On the right, the wooded valley of Calamity Creek has come close to the road. The valley follows the Calamity Creek Fault; springs and seepage along the fault water the trees. Two hundred yards ahead, blocky light gray limestone is exposed in roadcuts on the left, overlain by volcanic rocks, part of a sequence of limestone and calcareous tuff beds 300 feet thick in the Pruett. The upper 200 feet is nearly pure limestone, light gray to brown.

Cathedral Mountain (6,800 feet) is dead ahead from the wooded picnic area on the right. This is one of the best viewing angles for the most spectacular peak in the Big Bend (photograph on page 205 and cover). A half-mile beyond the picnic area, the road crosses from Pruett limestone on to a Lower Basalt, the Sheep Canyon Basalt. This basalt consists of a series of basalt flows separated by thin tuff breccia, weathered basalt and limestone layers between 1 and 15 feet thick. The surrounding hills are typical of lava terrain, rounded and rough, with occasional lava exposures. Two miles ahead, a roadcut exposes beautiful pink tuff in the basalt. The upper 4 feet of basalt are white on the surface.

The pullout just beyond the roadcut is a good viewpoint for the mountains to the west. Cienega Mountain (6,580 feet) at 10 o'clock is a mushroom-shaped laccolith, part of a 12 ½ square mile quartz trachyte intrusion. Cliffs 600 feet high face the upper part of the intrusion, a dome measuring about 3 miles by 2. Little Cienega Mountain (5,390 feet) at 9 o'clock is a stock, created when the intrusion, pushing up from below, found a weak spot in the overlying rocks.

The bridge over Calamity Creek is 56 miles from Study Butte, 22 miles from Alpine. The Calamity Creek Fault crosses the road about 200 yards beyond the bridge and downthrows basalt on the left 525 feet against Crossen trachyte on the right. The fault has been traced from Haley Mountain ahead to Elephant Mountain where it disappears into alluvium in Green Valley. Weak and broken rock along the fault has helped Calamity Creek cut a valley along the fault trace. The creek is spring-fed along this stretch and always has water in it.

Cathedral Mountain

Cathedral Mountain, 7 miles away at 12 o'clock from the bridge, is the most dramatic landform in this part of the Big Bend, an enormous block of volcanic and volcaniclastic strata standing almost 2,000 feet above its surroundings, 2 miles long, one mile wide and weighing nearly 4 billion tons. It has an upper spire and bench running east west for 2 miles and a lower bench running northwest for about 4½ miles. The upper bench is capped by 545 feet of Upper Basalt, above 450 feet of Tascotal Formation volcaniclastics. Haley's Peak forms a spire on the right. The spire is a block faulted and thrust up by an intrusion that crops out on the lower slopes. Mitchell Mesa welded tuff, 85 feet thick, caps the lower bench and overlays fine-grained rhyolitic tuff and volcaniclastic sedimentary rocks of the Duff Formation. The view from the bridge is almost at right angles to the upper bench. The northwest part of the lower bench can be seen from Cathedral Mountain Road ahead (photograph on page 205).

A mile beyond the Calamity Creek bridge, basalt overlies pink tuff in a roadcut. The heat of the basalt has baked the upper 12 inches of tuff into a hard white rock. If you look back at the 20 miles to Alpine sign, you can see the trace of the Calamity Creek Fault run down the valley of Calamity Creek just to the right of Elephant Mountain.

Nevill Mesa (5,050 feet) rises on the right to an uneven broken summit of basalt over Crossen Trachyte, 700 feet above the road. The mesa is on the far side of Calamity Creek Fault where strata are 525 feet higher than on this side, hence the mesa's prominence. On its east side a steep escarpment descends 950 feet through lavas and Pruett strata into Chalk Valley.

For the next 14 miles the road follows the valley of Ash Creek, a tributary of Calamity Creek. It comes down into the creek valley and then climbs out of it through nearly continuous roadcuts in Lower Basalt (photograph on page 206). More basalt crops out on the low scraggy hills. The tip of McIntyre Peak is on the horizon at 10 o'clock.

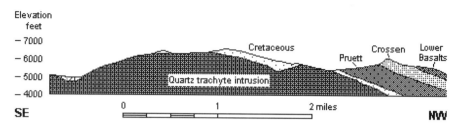

Section across Cienega Mountain

Cienega Mountain is at 7 o'clock from Calamity Creek Road. The cross-section above is drawn from this viewpoint. The intrusion is a trapdoor laccolith raised up from the left. The "door" is a sequence of light-colored Cretaceous limestone and sandstone beds dipping to the right, overlain by Pruett, Crossen and basalt strata. Goat Mountain is on its right flank.

The Cathedral Mountain Road junction is a wonderful viewpoint. Elephant Mountain is at 4 o'clock with Santiago Peak on its left shoulder, Kokernot Mesa at 5 o'clock, and Cienega Mountain at 7 o'clock with Goat Mountain to its right. This is one of the best views of Goat Mountain (6,480 feet) on Highway 118. The mountain is a rectangular, block, 3 miles long and one mile wide, standing 1,300 feet above the pediment at its base. It is capped by Upper Basalt, 270-foot thick, overlying Tascotal tuff, Mitchell Mesa welded tuff and Duff tuff, the same sequence as in Cathedral Mountain.

The upper bench and spire of Cathedral Mountain loom over the road at 8 o'clock. You can also see the lower bench of the mountain from here. It forms a long mesa running one mile northwest of the main body, followed by two buttes, one of which can be seen at 9 o'clock. The mesa and butte are about 600 feet above the flats, and are both capped by Mitchell Mesa welded tuff. Under the welded tuff, creamy white Duff strata crop out sporadically along the mesa and butte, as outlined in the drawing on the opposite page. Below the basalt on Haley's Peak, yellow Tascotal tuff and tuff breccia crops out in nearly vertical cliff about 100 feet high (photograph on page 205).

The Duff, Tascotal and Upper Basalt strata are thicker on Cathedral Mountain and Goat Mountain, 6 miles to its southwest, than elsewhere, and were probably deposited in a basin that began sinking during the Duff period. The thick basalt slowed down erosion and Cathedral and Goat Mountains are now the last outcrops of the younger volcanic rocks to remain in the southern Davis Mountains. The Upper Basalt lavas, the youngest lavas along Green Valley and the southern Davis Mountains, are

Cathedral Mountain from Cathedral Mountain Road

widespread, most notably on Tascotal Mesa and west, where basalts of the Rawls Formation, 26 to 23 million years old, crop out over an area 25 miles in diameter. Large outcrops also occur around and west of Marfa where they are classified as Petan Basalt; scattered outcrops are found near Alpine around the Paisano Volcano and in the Davis Mountains. None of the latter occurrences have been dated and are probably not related to the Rawls occurrences.

Christopher Henry and his co-authors in their paper on the Davis Mountains (see Reading List), propose that basaltic magma was present below the silica-rich rhyolitic and trachyte magmas throughout the time of Davis Mountains volcanic activity but was only able to come through the latter when they cooled and solidified. The time needed to solidify the silica-rich magmas was of the order of 100,000 to 200,000 years. Basalts, including Lower Basalt, were therefore extruded episodically during pauses in the silica-rich volcanism.

Haley Mountain (5,685 feet) is on the north skyline at 10 o'clock, looking rather like a sesame-seed hamburger bun. It is a trachyte sill, 300 feet thick, an offshoot of the McIntyre Peak intrusion. It rests on basalt on its north side and Duff strata elsewhere. Immediately to its right, McIntyre Peak (6,378 feet) is a high trachyte cone with a ragged rough top, part of an intrusion 3 miles long.

Mount Ord (6,700 feet) is at 3 o'clock from its roadside sign, the high point on an east-facing cuesta that continues on the skyline south to Elephant Mountain. The west side of the cuesta dips towards the road at nearly the same angle as a bed of Crossen trachyte, 265 feet thick at the Mount Ord summit. In places the lava has been eroded away, exposing soft Pruett tuff. The lava breaks off at the crest of the ridge, creating an escarpment to the east, 600 feet high at Mount Ord and 500 feet at Elephant Mountain, overlooking Chalk Valley, 2,300 feet below the Mount Ord summit. The section on the following page is from just east of McIntyre Peak to Mount Ord approximately through the roadside sign for Mount Ord. Highway 118 is near the base of a broad syncline between the two peaks.

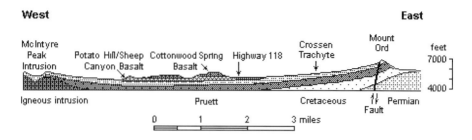

Section across syncline from McIntyre Peak to Mount Ord

Folding seems to have begun about 37 Ma when the Duff Formation was being deposited and was completed by the end of Tascotal deposition, 31 Ma, according to William McNulty.

A half-mile ahead, pinkish tuff overlain by Lower Basalt crops out in a roadcut on the right. A similar exposure is on the left side of the road three-quarters of a mile ahead. The lower 15 inches of lava has been altered by contact with the tuff and has weathered to a cream color.

Just beyond Mile High Road, the road crosses a saddle in which basalt is exposed in roadcuts on the left and right. The rock has been broken up by a number of small faults. The saddle (5,403 feet) is the divide between the Rio Grande and the Pecos River drainage basins, the highest point on Highway 118. Cathedral and Cienega Mountains can be glimpsed on the skyline at 9 o'clock a short distance ahead. The road runs along the base of a nepheline syenite intrusion on the right for the next mile. The intrusion has eroded into rocky hills up to 350 feet above the road.

The sharp pyramid-shaped trachyte intrusion of Smith Peak (5,764 feet) is at 3 o'clock from just beyond the North Double Diamond Pinion Drive entrance. The spectacular escarpment of a second Cathedral Mountain, the one in the Glass Mountains, is just to its left on the skyline, 12½ miles away. At 2 o'clock, light gray limestone hills dip away from Bird Mountain (6,140 feet), the highest point on the skyline. The very craggy bluff at 10 o'clock is the south end of another trachyte intrusion that runs parallel to the road for about 2 miles.

The Alpine Basin

A mile beyond the North Double Diamond Pinion Drive entrance, the road crests a Crossen Trachyte ridge at the top of Big Hill and descends 250 feet through trachyte roadcuts into the Alpine basin (photograph on page 206). The pullout on the right coming down the hill is a good

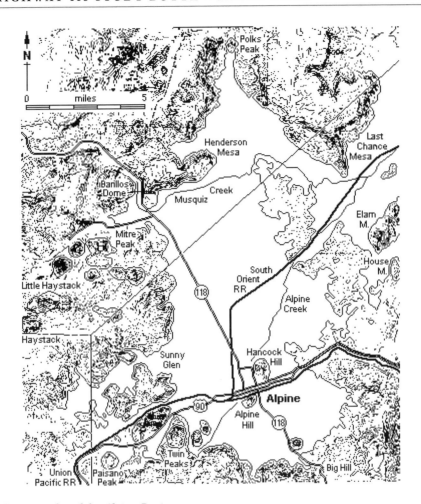

Physiography of the Alpine Basin

viewpoint for the fine panorama over the basin. Low rolling hills and
swales bottom the basin for the 5 miles from Big Hill to Alpine. From
Alpine to Polks Peak, the basin is a flat-bottomed plain 17 miles long and 7
miles wide. Although it has never been mapped in detail, the basin appears
to be mainly the result of erosion, similar to Green Valley and many other
flats in the Big Bend. Its southern part is a graben, as shown on the
geological map on the next page. A fault zone runs along the cliffs on the
west across the opening into Sunny Glen and displaces strata 1,250 feet
into the basin. Based on data from water wells drilled around Alpine, a
second fault appears to run through the west side of Hancock Hill towards
Musquiz Creek, displacing strata 850 feet down to the left at Hancock Hill.

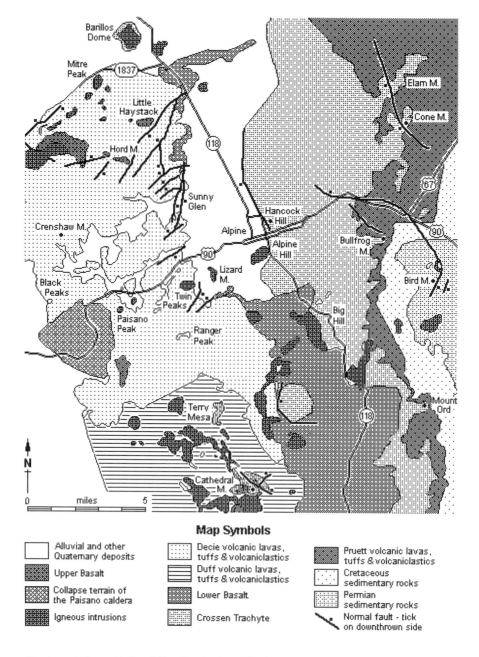

Geology: Mount Ord to Mitre Peak along Highway 118

The basin is bordered on the left by a succession of Decie Formation rhyolitic and trachytic lavas erupted from the Paisano volcanic center west of Alpine. They rise up to 1,300 feet above the basin floor. A number of intrusions, mostly trachytes, stand up above the lavas, including Ranger Peak at 10 o'clock, Twin Peaks at 12 o'clock, The Haystacks at 1 o'clock, and Castle Rock and Mitre Peak at 1:30 o'clock.

Decie lava cliffs continue on the western basin margin for 2 miles south of Highway 90. The margin then swings east across Lower Basalt outcrops and intrusions to Highway 118 at Big Hill. East of Big Hill, the basin boundary swings north to Musquiz Creek along a Crossen Trachyte ridge, a continuation of the ridge at Mount Ord.

The high point on the ridge between Highways 118 and 90 is Bullfrog Mountain (5,400 feet). North of Highway 90, the ridge is lower with isolated crests such as Cone, Horse and Elam Mountains on its eastern edge.

Down Big Hill, McIntyre Peak is at 9 o'clock from the entrance to the Que Decie Ranch on the left, very narrow and steep sided from this angle. An intrusive dike-like body of syenite outcrops at 4 o'clock. Further along, the 200-feet columnar lava cliffs on the left belong to the McIntyre Lava member of the Decie Formation and cap the eastern edge of the Paisano shield volcano. The cap is about 800 feet above the flat below.

A mile ahead on the right, the high rounded hill is an outlier of Lower Basalt overlying Crossen Trachyte. Alpine or "A" Hill at 11:30 o'clock is a trachyte intrusion.

Alpine

On entering Alpine, Highway 118 turns left on Avenue E and turns right on to 5th Street seven blocks west. The city began life around Kokernot Springs on the wagon trail between Chihuahua and the United States. Settlers arrived when the Galveston, Harrisburg and San Antonio Railway came through in 1882 and made Alpine a watering stop. The town quickly became a shipping point and supply center for ranching and was made county seat in 1884 when Brewster County was split off from Presidio County. In 1921, a summer normal school, eventually to become Sul Ross State University, began classes leading to an increase in the population from 921 in 1920 to 3,495 in 1930. Since then, the town has grown slowly. In 2000, the population was 5,786, Sul Ross is the largest employer, and ranching and tourism are important industries.

Leaving Alpine on Highway 118 north, the basin is a plain floored by a thin layer of alluvium underlain by Lower Basalt on the left and Crossen

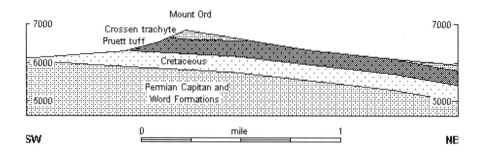

Mount Ord from north of Alpine on Highway 118

trachyte on the right. A deep water well drilled near Alpine Cemetery just south of town intersected 50 feet of alluvium, 600 feet of Lower Basalt with interbedded tuffs, 211 feet of Crossen trachyte, 544 feet of Pruett tuffs and entered Cretaceous strata 1,405 feet below the surface (Alpine on the cross-section on page 174). Hancock Hill (4,925 feet), with Sul Ross State University on its flanks, is on the right, an up faulted block of Crossen trachyte about 500 feet above the plain.

On the left, Decie lava cliffs form an escarpment up to 1,000 feet high. They may have extended further east when first created but probably not much further, as the lavas are quite erosion resistant. Two lava flows with underlying tuffs crop out on the escarpment, the Morrow and the McIntyre Lavas named after the Morrow-McIntyre Ranch west of Alpine. The contact between the two dips north from about 5,250 feet elevation at Alpine to 4,800 feet at Mitre Peak. Dark outcrops of Lower Basalt appear intermittently along the base of the escarpment. Canyons have developed at intervals in the cliffs, the deepest being Sunny Glen, 4 miles northwest of town.

Four miles north of town, the limestone slopes of the Glass Mountains dominate the skyline at 5 o'clock. The rounded top of Bird Mountain at 5 o'clock is at the north end of the Del Norte range. The sharp peak of Mount Ord and the spire of Cathedral Mountain are to its right. Mount Ord (6,803 feet), the highest of the Del Norte Mountains, is visible from most of Alpine. The cross-section above shows it to be almost a cuesta, capped by Crossen Trachyte. The west slope of the mountain is nearly the dip slope of the strata while the east slope is an escarpment.

The beautiful rolling alluvial plain on the right stretches across low rounded hills of the Crossen trachyte ridge to the higher hills at the eastern edge of the Crossen exposures. Elam Mountain (4,940 feet) is the highest at about 3 o'clock; Horse Mountain (4,890 feet) is to its right.

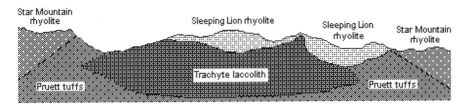

Section across the Barillos Dome from the ridge overlooking Musquiz Creek

The South Orient railroad follows a valley 350 feet deep cut through the ridge by Alpine Creek at 2:30 o'clock. The northern basin is fully visible up to Polks Peak (5,304 feet), the hat-like butte 14 miles away at 1 o'clock.

Hord Mountain (5,940 feet) and Little Haystack (5,685 feet) are on the skyline at 9 o'clock from the Williams Ranch entrance, 7 miles north of Alpine. Both are capped by Upper Basalt overlying McIntyre Lava. The narrow deep canyon below Hord Mountain runs southwest for about 3 miles. It is probably a fault site; the caprock on the right of the canyon is about 80 feet lower than on the left, indicating a displacement down to the right. The Morrow Lava caps the escarpment here and dips to the north at about 5½ degrees.

An outcrop of Lower Basalt crosses the road about the point where it bears left, and creates a low ridge running parallel to Musquiz Creek for 5 miles at 3 o'clock. The Musquiz Creek valley on its north is about 120 feet below its crest. The valley is probably the result of erosion but is nearly in line with a fault on the left of the road and so may be a downfaulted block.

The Barillos Dome, at 11:30 0'clock from the top of the ridge, is cored by a trachyte laccolith intruded into Pruett tuffs and Star Mountain rhyolite. The intrusion is lighter colored than the surrounding volcanics and stands out as a lozenge-shaped body with a sharp peak on its right. Several light gray Pruett tuff beds can be seen dipping away from the intrusion at 30 degrees on its right. Lava beds of Star Mountain rhyolite overlie the Pruett tuffs, also dipping to the right and forming hogbacks. Star Mountain rhyolite is similar in age (37 Ma), appearance and composition to the Crossen trachyte; the latter dips under the former around the dome and hence is slightly older. The age of the Barillos intrusion is unknown but the Weston Dome, a similar intrusion a few miles north has been dated at 33 Ma and that age seems reasonable for the Barillos Dome too.

Henderson Mesa (5,616 feet) on the right in front is capped by hard rhyolitic lava of the Sleeping Lion Formation. The Sleeping Lion Formation is slightly younger than the Decie lavas, originating in the vicinity of Fort Davis. The escarpment has several scars from erosion, the most prominent at 1:30. The cap rock was undercut and collapsed as tuff under it washed away. Some smaller scars are near the right end of the mesa, all at a soft tuff horizon in the escarpment. Star Mountain Rhyolite, also very resistant to erosion, caps Last Chance Mesa to the right of Henderson Mesa.

Mitre Peak (6,190 feet), Antelope Peak (5,848 feet) and Castle Rock (5,945 feet), are at 9:30 o'clock from the junction with FM 1837. The three rhyolite bodies, and a fourth smaller one hidden behind them, have been intruded along a fault cropping out just to their north, the fault that may have created the Musquiz Creek valley. Mitre Peak's rough surface is due to erosion along jointing. Just to the right of Mitre Peak, a dike perhaps related to the intrusion forms a ridge in the foreground.

The enormous twin bulks of the Haystacks are on the skyline behind Castle Rock. The peak on the right (6,895 feet) is the tallest in the Alpine area. The other directly to its left (6,670 feet) is less bulky. The two mountains are trachyte intrusions from a single igneous body below. Their age is unknown but a nearby intrusion was dated by the A^{39}/A^{40} method at 34.6 Ma, about 700,000 years after volcanic activity ended in the Davis Mountains but 1½ million years before the Weston Dome and perhaps the Barillos Dome formed.

The lava flows and ash tuffs of the Paisano volcanic center end at the FM 1837 junction and Highway 118 enters terrain underlain by similar rocks from other Davis Mountains volcanic centers. Highway 118 continues on to Fort Davis and through the Davis Mountains to Interstate 10 at Kent, a most beautiful drive.

Hwy 90 Alpine – Marfa Lights Viewing Center

18 miles

This section of highway begins in the Alpine basin surrounded by rounded volcanic hills. It enters the harsh and craggy canyons of the Paisano Volcano where columns of jointed lava cap ragged cliff tops and passes into the volcano's central caldera. The collapse that formed the caldera created great confusion on the surface, landslides and mudflows creating what geologists call chaotic or collapse terrain, all of it seen in roadcuts along the way. The road emerges at Paisano Pass on to the beautiful grassy, undulating Marfa plain, where wonderful vistas extend for many miles to the west and south. Highway 90 has quite heavy traffic and many blind corners. It is not safe to stop except where there are parking facilities or where you can park well off the road.

Mileages are measured from the intersection of Highways 90 and 118 South in Alpine. The strata along this section are described in the table on pages 176-7.

Twin Peaks

At the Big Bend Sportsman Club entrance, 3 miles west of Alpine, Lizard Mountain (4,976 feet) is the craggy iguana-shaped ridge at 9 o'clock. Ranger Peak (6,246 feet) is at 9:30 o'clock 2½ miles away and Twin Peaks (6,133 feet and 6,112 feet), also called Twin Sisters, are the double peaks at 10 o'clock, 1,400 feet above the road. The diagram below illustrates the Twin Peaks structure, a quartz trachyte intrusion set in Morrow lavas and tuffs.

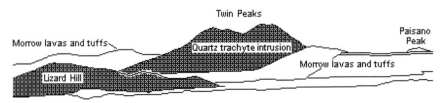

Twin Peaks from the Big Bend Sportsman Club entrance 3 miles west of Alpine

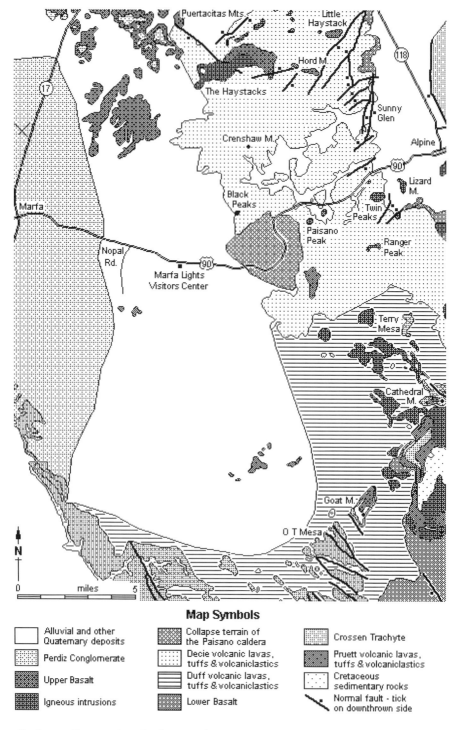

Map Symbols

Alluvial and other Quaternary deposits	Collapse terrain of the Paisano caldera	Crossen Trachyte
Perdiz Conglomerate	Decie volcanic lavas, tuffs & volcaniclastics	Pruett volcanic lavas, tuffs & volcaniclastics
Upper Basalt	Duff volcanic lavas, tuffs & volcaniclastics	Cretaceous sedimentary rocks
Igneous intrusions	Lower Basalt	Normal fault - tick on downthrown side

Geology: Alpine to Marfa along Highway 9

Between Lizard Mountain and Twin Peaks, a 450-foot high Lower Basalt hill is perhaps domed by a hidden intrusion.

Paisano Volcano

Four miles west of Alpine, a fault scarp runs north along the skyline on the right of the road. The fault, which drops strata 1,250 feet into the Alpine basin at Sunny Glen, is intermittently exposed between there and the railway line. It is on the eastern edge of the Paisano Volcano, in which lava erupted through fissures rather than a central vent, and created a shield-like body, 15 miles in diameter. When eruptions ended at 36 Ma, lava in the fissures solidified into dikes, about a thousand of which crops out in the volcano today. Quartz trachyte flows of Morrow Lava cap the mesas on both sides of the road, underlain by Morrow tuffs with Lower Basalt cropping out at the base of the escarpments. The Paisano Rhyolite appears to be absent here (see Decie Formation description on page 176).

A ridge separates the highway from the railway line. Faults in both sides of the ridge have produced weak rock for erosion to exploit, creating canyons and the ridge. The latter is crowned by hoodoos of light greenish-gray Morrow lava up to 300 feet thick, 750 feet above the road (photograph on page 207). The large boulder at the roadside under the second hoodoo came from the cave above. Occasional outcrops of light gray tuff can be seen on the ridge flanks.

A much jointed quartz trachyte lava flow crops out in a roadcut on the right a mile after the road enters the volcano. It has a 10-ft thick dike of inclusion-filled tuff near its east end. A narrow cockscomb-like dike comes down from Twin Peaks opposite the picnic area, 6 miles from Alpine. It runs parallel to the road for the next 1½ miles, forming the crest of a discontinuous ridge. Several dikes crop out on ridges on the right.

Just beyond the picnic area, a block of yellowish-gray bedded Morrow Tuff is downfaulted against pale pink to dark red rhyolite. The rhyolite contains many inclusions towards the west of the roadcut, some as large as 3 inches in diameter. This is the first appearance of the rhyolite, which underlies Morrow strata. In places, it is a very pretty, spotted rock, light bluish gray on fresh surfaces. The first geologist to sample it was A. Osann, a German national who joined the Geological Survey of Texas in 1891. He described it in his report in the Fourth Annual Report of the Survey published in 1892. He called it *paisanite*, after Paisano Pass. The spots are clumps of the mineral arfvedsonite, an amphibole.

The high walls around the picnic area are capped by the McIntyre member of the Decie Formation underlain by Morrow lavas and tuffs. At 2 o'clock, a butte is in the final stages of erosion. In a few years, the cap will have disappeared.

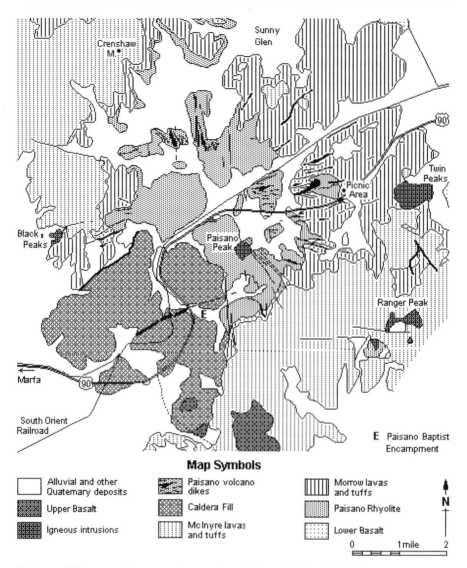

Map Symbols

☐ Alluvial and other Quaternary deposits	▨ Paisano volcano dikes	▥ Morrow lavas and tuffs
▓ Upper Basalt	▨ Caldera Fill	▨ Paisano Rhyolite
▓ Igneous intrusions	▥ McInyre lavas and tuffs	∷ Lower Basalt

E Paisano Baptist Encampment

N

0   1 mile   2

Paisano Volcano and surroundings; adapted from Parker (1979a).

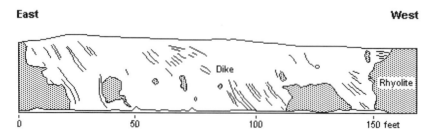

Striations in a dike wall on the right of the road show the flow direction of magma

In front, the elegant rounded silhouette of Paisano Peak (6,085 feet) rises 1,050 feet above the road. It is a nepheline syenite plug intruded into the Paisano Rhyolite after volcanic activity had ended (see diagram on page 228).

A half-mile ahead, at the top of the rise, outcrops of welded ash-flow Morrow tuff include boulders several feet across. An attractive circular inclusion of trachyte, 3 feet in diameter is exposed in the left-hand roadcut. No trachyte erupted in the volcano before the Morrow tuff, so this and other trachyte inclusions must have been brought up from the earth's crust below the Decie rocks. The tuff is bedded in places. Its color on fresh surfaces varies greatly from pink to dark green and yellowish-gray. More Morrow tuff is in a roadcut a quarter-mile ahead and includes some laminated rhyolite inclusions.

At the top of the next incline, 7.8 miles from Alpine, high roadcuts on either side bracket the road in which very shattered spotted paisanite is exposed. The roadcut on the left runs along the edge of a quartz trachyte dike cutting the rhyolite. Striations in the gray wall show that the dike flowed at roughly 60 degrees up to the east as shown in the diagram opposite which was sketched from photographs.

The railway line comes into view on the right at the Gage Holland ranch entrance. Crenshaw Mountain (5,965 feet) on the skyline at 2 o'clock across Sunny Glen is capped by McIntyre Lava, as are the uplands to its left. Just after the ranch entrance, a low roadcut shows welded blue gray Morrow tuff grading into poorly welded cream-colored tuff at the west end of the cut. As the road veers to the left, roadcuts on both sides of the road expose large red welded tuff blocks and angular boulders in landslide flows of light pinkish gray tuffaceous material.

The Paisano Caldera

Following the removal of magma from beneath a volcano, the volcano itself often collapses, forming a broken jumble of angular rocks called *breccia*, and creating a caldera, a basin-shaped depression. That appears to have happened in the Paisano Volcano. An area of broken-up lava and tuff 3 miles in diameter southwest of Paisano Peak is thought to be a caldera.

The caldera formed after eruption of the McIntyre Tuff and before eruption of the McIntyre Lava; strata older than the latter are very broken up, strata younger only slightly so. Collapse was uneven; strata fell 1,000 feet into the structure west of Paisano Peak but at other places on its boundary there is little displacement into the caldera. The caldera margin crosses the road obliquely at the Forker-Gage Ranch entrance on the left and opposite a railroad bridge on the right, 9.6 miles from Alpine. The

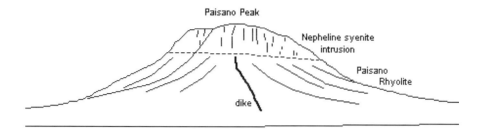

A dike runs up the side of Paisano Peak to the base of the intrusion.

bluff ahead on the left is in the caldera. The rounded hill at 3 o'clock is a rhyolite dome outside the caldera; yellowish rhyolite crops out on its summit. The smooth yellow hills to its right also appear to be rhyolite domes. The caldera boundary runs along the low ground between the railway line and the high hills on the skyline at about 12:30 o'clock, crossing the road again near the South Orient Railroad line 6 miles ahead, as shown on the map on page 226. Photographs of several of the rock types in the caldera are shown on pages 207-8.

The left wall of the next roadcut thee-quarters of a mile ahead, shows the tremendous variety in the Paisano caldera. Much of the wall overhangs the ground below and is best viewed from the right side of the road. It begins on the left with a fossil mudflow intruded by a dike running up to the left at 45 degrees, next a patch of welded volcanic breccia in red brown tuff, followed by large block of volcanic breccia between two sections of poorly welded yellow gray tuff 10 and 3 feet wide, then a section of very poorly welded tuff with red-brown block of volcanic breccia, and at the west end red-brown welded tuff. The random way blocks are oriented and the jumbled up nature of the outcrop suggests that they resulted from a landslide into the caldera.

Just beyond the Paisano Baptist Encampment entrance, a thick dike exposed in a roadcut creates a ridge on the right. This dike, 3 miles long, is one of the largest mapped in the volcano. The 500-foot high walls at 9 o'clock behind the encampment are on the western edge of the caldera where the collapse was around 1,000 feet. A little ahead, reddish tuff containing chaotic accumulations of coarse angular volcanic rocks, overlies light gray tuff in a roadcut on the left, followed by mudslide, volcanic breccia and welded tuff in short roadcuts on both sides of road.

Low mounds of volcanic breccia are on both sides of the road at the Presidio County sign, 12½ miles from Alpine. In the roadcut just beyond the sign, multiple dikes cut fine-grained rhyolite. One dike was an ash-flow feeder vent through which volcanic ash reached the surface. This is shown by the eutaxitic structure of blue-gray compacted pumice parallel to the dike walls. In a eutaxitic structure, pumice fragments are compacted into parallel disc-shaped lenses while still viscous.

A ranch entrance on the left 13 miles from Alpine is followed by a short roadcut through megabreccia containing large blocks still nearly horizontal. Some of these blocks may have slid downhill in landslides. To the left of one, you can see a jumble of angular lava blocks in a fine matrix, a fossil mudslide.

A historical plaque marks the summit of Paisano Pass (5,074 feet). When the Galveston, Harrisburg and San Antonio Railroad built its track in 1882, Paisano Pass was said to be the highest point on the line between New Orleans and Portland, Oregon. It is also claimed that it is the highest point on Highway 90 between Florida and California.

The hill at 9 o'clock is in the caldera and capped by Upper Basalt. A short distance ahead, 14 miles from Alpine, the road crosses the South Orient Railroad. This line, originally the Kansas City, Mexico and Orient Railway, was built to run the 1,600 miles between Kansas City, Missouri, and Topolobampo, Mexico. It was completed to Presidio in 1930, sharing tracks with what is now the Union Pacific line from Alpine to Paisano Pass. In 2000, the Texas Department of Transportation purchased the line from its previous owners and leased it for 40 years to the Mexican-owned company Texas Pacifico Transportation Ltd, which renovating the track.

Just beyond the railway bridge, the road crosses the western boundary of the caldera on to the Marfa plain and one of the great vistas in the Big Bend opens up. The plain east and south of Marfa is underlain by Tertiary lavas and volcaniclastics and by large expanses of a coarse conglomerate, the Perdiz Conglomerate, created by erosion from the Chinati Mountains between 29 and 25 Ma. The Chinati Mountains border the plain on the southwest. Their highest point, Chinati Peak (7,728 feet), is the whale-backed mountain on the horizon at 10:30, 44 miles southwest of here. It is built up of large intrusions and a succession of lava flows erupted from the Chinati volcanic center very similar in composition to those of the Paisano Volcano. To its left, the summit of the enormous rhyolite dome of the Cienega Mountains (5,223 feet) is on the horizon. The volcanic Bofecillos Mountains form the southern boundary of the plain, 50 miles away over the horizon. The plain extends north to Fort Davis, with the Puertacitas Mountains encroaching on it just north of Marfa. It continues northwest of Marfa to Van Horn between Sierra Vieja and the Van Horn Mountains and the Davis and Wylie Mountains and then on into New Mexico at Dell City, 200 miles away. A shallow gravel-filled graben underlies the plain from 10 miles northwest of Marfa to beyond Dell City.

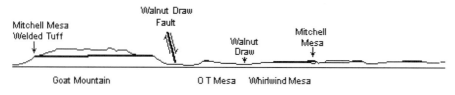

Goat Mountain from the Marfa Lights Viewing Center

Capote Peak (6,212 feet), capped by Mitchell Mesa welded tuff, is at the southern end of Sierra Vieja on the horizon at 12 o'clock. The high cliffs of Mount Livermore (8,378 feet), also known as Baldy Peak, are at 1:30 o'clock, 31 miles away. The highest of the Davis Mountains, and the second highest peak in Texas, it is built up of lava flows and intrusive sills with a light-colored volcanic dome on its summit, perhaps 1,000 feet high. The dome is completely without vegetation, hence the name Baldy Peak.

The Marfa Lights Viewing Center is a good place to stop and look over the area. Using Highway 90 west as 12 o'clock, the twin Haystack peaks (6,895 and 6,670 feet) are at 3:30 o'clock. Both are trachyte intrusions, two of the largest mountain masses around Alpine. Nearer the road, the Black Peaks, several small dark gray-brown intrusions, stick up noticeably out of the surrounding Morrow Lava at 4:30 o'clock. A sample was dated at 36.9 Ma, slightly older than the Paisano Volcano. The Puertacitas Mountains (6,285 feet), on the skyline at 2:30 o'clock, consist of three small brown-tinted intrusions into Upper Basalt.

Paisano Peak is at 5:30 o'clock and Cathedral Mountain at 7 o'clock. The large mass of Cienega Mountain (6,562 feet) is just south of Cathedral Mountain. The massive, relatively flat-topped Goat Mountain (6,608 feet) is at 8 o'clock. Cathedral, Cienega and Goat Mountains are described in the Study Butte – Alpine section.

To the right of Goat Mountain, a series of faults displace strata down to the southwest. The first such fault is the Walnut Draw Fault, just to the right of Goat Mountain, as shown on the drawing above. The welded tuff, which crops out high on Goat Mountain, is brought down 700 feet. It becomes the caprock on O T Mesa (5,570feet) about 19 miles away at 8:30 o'clock, still 650 feet above the plain. Walnut Draw, on its southwest flank, descends 600 feet to Green Valley through Rustlers Gap.

Beyond Walnut Draw, Mitchell Mesa is on the horizon followed by Whirlwind Mesa at about 8 o'clock, both at about the same elevation as O T Mesa. The mesas die away to their right as the welded tuff caprock is brought down to the level of the plain by further faulting.

U.S. Hwy 67 Alpine - Fort Stockton

67 Miles

Highway 67 from Alpine to Fort Stockton climbs over low Crossen trachyte ridges as it leaves the Alpine basin and turns left 8 miles east of town to run northeast between the Davis Mountains volcanic field and the Glass Mountains for 20 miles and then between low Cretaceous limestone mesas of the Stockton Plateau to Fort Stockton.

Mileages are measured from the intersection of Highways 90 and 118 South in Alpine. Volcanic strata in the Alpine area are described in the table on page 176, Cretaceous and Permian strata north of Alpine in the table on page 38.

Fine panoramas stretch across the Alpine basin to the left as you leave town. Mitre Peak is on the horizon 12 miles away at 8 o'clock, the Barillos Dome slightly to its right. Next is Henderson Mesa, capped by hard rhyolite of the Sleeping Lion Formation, followed by the double summit of Polks Peak and then Last Chance Mesa on the eastern edge of the Davis Mountains volcanic field. The cap rock of the latter is Star Mountain Rhyolite, similar in age and character to the Crossen trachyte and also very erosion-resistant.

The highway crosses the eastern boundary of the Alpine basin beginning at two miles east of town. It climbs over two ridges of Crossen trachyte tilted to the west. Trachyte is exposed in several roadcuts in the ridges, in some severely altered by weathering and turned largely into clay, in others mostly unaltered. About four miles from Alpine, at the summit of the second ridge, the road veers to the right. Here, a fault crosses the highway and runs down a swale towards Mitre Peak, displacing strata at least 500 feet down to the left. Thus the summit of the attractive whale-backed ridge on the left is 700 feet below the summit of Bullfrog Mountain, ahead on the right, although Crossen trachyte caps both. The fault continues south along the base of the Del Norte Mountains for some 25 miles. It forms the western boundary of a shallow graben or down-dropped block between the Del Norte and Glass Mountains, the northern part of which is shown on the map on the next page.

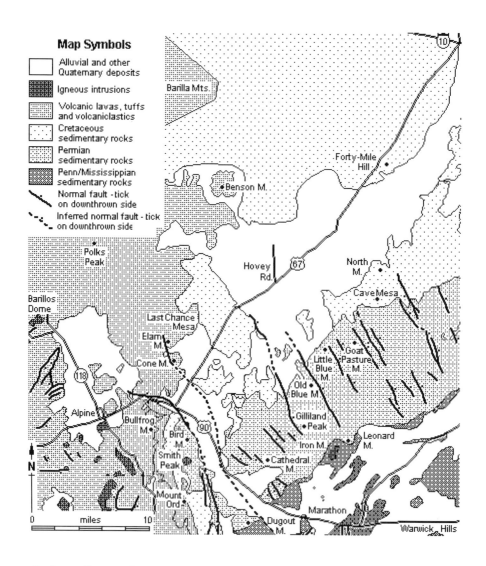

Map Symbols

☐ Alluvial and other Quaternary deposits

▨ Igneous intrusions

☐ Volcanic lavas, tuffs and volcaniclastics

☐ Cretaceous sedimentary rocks

☐ Permian sedimentary rocks

▨ Penn/Mississippian sedimentary rocks

⟋ Normal fault - tick on downthrown side

⟍ Inferred normal fault - tick on downthrown side

Geology: Alpine to Interstate 10 along Highway 67

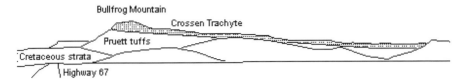

Bullfrog Mountain showing Crossen Trachyte dipping down slope; from a photograph taken 4 miles north of Highway 90

Round the corner, Crossen caprock dips at 6 degrees off Bullfrog Mountain (5,400 feet), the butte with the radio towers on its summit. The mountain is a continuation of the structure seen at Mount Ord, nine miles south, where strata sloped steeply down from the crest of a ridge (see cross-sections on page 216 and 220). Strata west of the northern Del Norte Mountains were folded between 37 and 31 Ma; Bullfrog Mountain is on the eastern flank of one of these folds, a low syncline.

In the hills to the right of the junction of Highways 90 and 67, Cretaceous Washita Group limestones dip to the west under volcanic strata. Turning left on to Highway 67, the low ridge to the right is of Crossen trachyte. At this point the road is still in the shallow graben described earlier. Cathedral Mountain (6,220 feet) at 3 o'clock on the skyline is one of the highest points in the Glass Mountains, 1,900 feet above the road.

The northeastern graben boundary crosses Highway 67 shortly before the Benge Road intersection, 4½ miles north of Highway 90. Crossen trachyte caps Cone Mountain (4,621 feet) at 7:30 o'clock, Horse Mountain (4,890 feet) at 9 o'clock and Elam Mountain (4,940 feet) at 9:30 o'clock. The graben boundary fault runs to the right of Cone Mountain and to the left of the other two. It has a displacement of about 300 feet down to the left.

On the right of the road, low hills and ridges of Washita and Fredericksburg Group limestones appear intermittently, the most prominent of which is Pate Peak (4,449 feet), a mile away at 3 o'clock and Carson Mountain (4,587 feet), 3 miles away behind it. Both rise about 400 feet above road level. These hills are brought up by a low anticline, a continuation of the Del Norte Mountain monocline, which becomes this anticline north of Bird Mountain.

Seven miles north of Highway 90, the road climbs up a northwest-trending anticline with Fredericksburg limestone exposed at its crest. This anticline lines up with Glass Mountain folding and is younger than the Del Norte monocline. The mesas behind Elam Mountain at 9 o'clock are on the

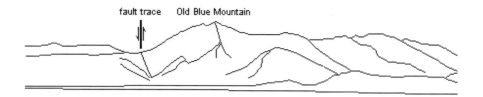

Old Blue Mountain from Hovey Road intersection

eastern edge of the Davis Mountains volcanic field. The nearest, Last Chance Mesa, 8 miles away, is capped by a lava bed of Star Mountain Rhyolite 275 feet thick, at its highest point rising about 1,000 feet above the road. To its north at 10 o'clock, the Barilla Mountains, another lava-capped line of mesas, can be seen on the skyline about 20 miles away. Ten miles north of Highway 90, Antelope Draw has cut a channel diagonally through the anticline. Two miles ahead, the road veers right and descends a small fault scarp on the north side of the anticline.

Hovey Road, 16½ miles north of Highway 90 on the left, leads to Hovey, an abandoned settlement and railroad station on the South Orient Railroad. The jagged north face of Old Blue Mountain (6,286 feet), 1,000 feet high, is at 4 o'clock, 9 miles from the Hovey Road intersection. An asymmetrical anticline, almost a monocline, runs along the crest of the mountain ridge. On its right, it raises strata at least 1,000 feet. On its left, a fault runs up a gully as shown in the sketch above and brings strata down 600 feet. The anticline moves the crest of Old Blue about 2 miles northwest of the other high crests in the Glass Mountains making it more prominent from Highway 67. Old Blue can be dark blue, dark gray, light gray or silver depending on the light and the time of day.

Little Blue Mountain (5,228 feet), at 3 o'clock, is slightly higher than the rest of the ridge. Gilliland Canyon is on its left and, on the other side of the canyon, Goat Pasture Mountain (5,017 feet), the last of the high summits. Northeast of this point, the Glass Mountains veer off to the east and become quite modest hills.

Highway 67 crosses alluvial flats from Hovey Road to Forty-Mile Hill, 33 miles north of Highway 90 with only occasional low limestone hills west of the road. On the right, the skyline has broken Cretaceous mesas and buttes north of the Glass Mountains, North Mountain (4,302 feet) and Cave Mesa (4,421 feet) among others. The elevation where Highway 67 crosses the South Orient railway line, 9 miles northeast of Hovey Road, is 3,481 feet, almost exactly 1,000 feet below Alpine, elevation 4,458 feet. The descent has been so gradual to be almost imperceptible.

Washita limestone crops out on Forty-Mile Hill (3,820 feet) and in low hills and ridges between the road and the volcanic Barillas Mountains at 9 o'clock. One possible reason why erosion is not more advanced here is that overlying volcanic strata may have been eroded off only recently and not enough time has elapsed for the usual Stockton Plateau mesa landscape to develop. Scattered mesas, such as Twelve Mile Mesa (3,735 feet), 10 miles away at 2 o'clock, do occur east of the highway, the higher ones capped by Washita strata. The underlying Fredericksburg limestone caps Triple Butte, 2 miles ahead on the right and appears in scattered outcrops and roadcuts in the 13 miles to Interstate 10.

Glossary

Words in italics are defined in the glossary.

alkali Said of *igneous* rock with more sodium and or potassium than is required to form feldspar with the available silica.

alkali feldspar A group of minerals containing the *alkali metals* sodium and or potassium but little calcium.

alkali metal Any of the elements lithium, potassium, sodium, rubidium or cesium.

alluvial fan A low gently-sloping mass of loose *alluvium,* shaped like a fan, left by a stream at the point where it comes out of a narrow mountain valley into a plain or broad valley.

alluvium Sand, clay, silt or gravel deposited recently and unconsolidated, i.e. not cemented together.

anticline A fold, generally convex up, whose core contains older rocks.

anticlinorium A series of *anticlines* and *synclines* that together form a gentle arch or *anticline.*

ash-fall tuff *Tuff* created by airborne volcanic ash falling from an ash cloud erupted from a volcano.

ash-flow tuff *Tuff* created from an ash flow, a mixture of volcanic gases and particles, usually hot, that flows out from explosive viscous *magma* in a volcanic fissure or crater; synonymous with *pyroclastic flow.*

basalt A dark-colored igneous rock composed mainly of calcic plagioclase and pyroxene; the fine-grained equivalent of *gabbro.*

breccia A coarse-grained rock made up of angular broken rock fragments held together by mineral cement or in a fine-grained matrix. A breccia differs from a *conglomerate* in that the fragments have sharp edges and unworn corners.

caldera A large basin-shaped volcanic depression.

calcite The principal component of limestone, calcium carbonate $CaCO_3$.

chalcedony A *cryptocrystalline* variety of quartz found in *chert* and in cavities and fissures in rocks.

chert A hard, dense, *microcrystalline* or *cryptocrystalline sedimentary* rock composed mainly of quartz. It may contain *opal* or *chalcedony*.

claystone A weakly *indurated, sedimentary* rock made up of mainly clay particles i.e. those with diameters of less than 0.01 millimeter.

collapse breccia *Breccia* formed by the collapse of rock overlying an opening such as a *magma* chamber or *intrusion*.

collapse caldera A *caldera* created by the collapse of a *magma* chamber through the removal of *magma* by volcanic explosions or lava eruptions, or by the removal of *magma* through subterranean pathways.

conglomerate A coarse-grained *sedimentary* rock, composed of rounded or sub-angular fragments of rock larger than 2 mm in diameter, set in a fine-grained matrix of sand or silt and commonly cemented by calcium carbonate, iron oxides, silica or hardened clay.

cryptocrystalline Said of a rock in which individual crystals are too small to be seen under an optical microscope, although they may be seen under an electron microscope.

crystalline A rock composed of minerals that have a crystalline structure and contain no glass.

cuesta A hill or ridge with a gentle slope conforming to the bed or beds that form it on one side and a steep slope on the other formed by outcrops of resistant rocks, the formation of the ridge being controlled by the *differential erosion* of the gently inclined strata.

dike A broad, tabular *igneous intrusion* that cuts across the bedding or foliation of the rock into which it was intruded.

differential erosion Erosion that occurs at varying rates caused by differences in the hardness or resistance of rocks; softer or weaker rocks are eroded more quickly than harder or more resistant rocks.

dolomite A common mineral $CaMg(CO_3)_2$; the word is also used for a variety of limestone rich in the mineral. The process by which limestone is transformed into dolomite is **dolomitization**. It usually occurs when water rich in magnesium, seawater for example, percolates through limestone.

evaporite A rock composed of minerals that crystallized from salt water or other solutions as they evaporated. Evaporites include gypsum, rock salt, dolomite and various nitrates and borates.

exfoliation The process by which concentric scales or shells of rock are stripped from the surface of a large rock mass.

extrusive rock   An *igneous* rock formed from *magma* that has erupted onto the surface of the earth; includes *lavas, pyroclastic flows* and volcanic ash.

fault scarp A steep slope or cliff formed by movement along a fault and corresponding to the exposed surface of the fault before it was modified by weathering or erosion.

felsic Said of an *igneous* rock rich in feldspars and silica, a light-colored rock. It is the complement of *mafic*.

gabbro A dark-colored *plutonic igneous* rock composed mainly of calcic feldspar and augite, the approximate equivalent of *basalt*.

graben A through or basin bounded on both sides by normal faults dipping into the graben and which has moved down relative to the adjoining fault blocks. See also *horst*.

granite A quartz-bearing *felsic plutonic* rock, the intrusive equivalent of rhyolite.

groundmass The material between *phenocrysts* in a *porphyritic igneous* rock. It is finer grained than the *phenocrysts* and may be crystalline, glassy or both.

half graben A basin bounded on one side by a normal fault.

hogback A ridge with a sharp summit and steep slopes of nearly equal inclination on either side, resembling in outline a hog's back.

hoodoo A column, pillar or pinnacle of rock created in an region of sporadic heavy rainfall by differential erosion of horizontal strata of differing resistance to weathering. Often occurs in grotesque or eccentric forms.

horst A block of the earth's crust that is bounded on opposite sides by faults dipping away from the block and has moved upward relative to the two adjoining blocks. See also *graben*.

igneous rock A rock made from molten or partly molten material, i.e. *magma*, that has cooled and solidified.

indurated Said of a rock hardened or consolidated by pressure, cementation or heat.

intrusion A rock that has formed from a *magma* that has intruded into pre-existing rock.

laccolith An *igneous intrusion* parallel to the bedding into which it was intruded except for its roof which is domed.

lahar A mudflow, consisting mainly of volcanic rocks and debris, on the flanks of a volcano.

lava *Magma* that comes to the earth's surface through a volcanic vent or fissure.

mafic Said of an *igneous* rock that is composed of minerals rich in iron and magnesium, a dark-colored rock. It is the complement of *felsic.*

magma Naturally occurring mobile rock material, generated within the earth and capable of being extruded and intruded, from which *igneous* rocks are derived through cooling. It may or may not contain suspended solids such as crystals and rock fragments.

microcrystalline Said of a rock in which the crystals are too small to be seen by the naked eye.

nepheline An *alkali* silicate of the feldspathoid group (Na,K)[AlSiO₄].

nepheline syenite A plutonic rock composed of *alkali feldspar* and *nepheline* and perhaps *alkali mafic* minerals; the intrusive equivalent of phonolite (see TAS diagram on page 21). Nepheline syenite or phonolite intrusions are found in the Trans-Pecos along a zone from the Black Hills east of Persimmon Gap to the Cornubas Mountains in New Mexico and include Santiago Peak, Black Mesa, Elephant Mountain and Paisano Peak.

normal fault A fault in which the hanging or upper wall has dropped relative to the foot or lower wall.

opal $SiO_4.nH_2O$; deposited from silica-bearing water at low temperatures; typically iridescent, found in cracks and cavities in igneous rocks. The transparent colored varieties are valued as gemstones.

outlier An area or group of rocks surrounded by older rocks.

pediment A gently-sloping broad erosion surface in a semi-arid region at the base of an abrupt and receding mountain front or plateau escarpment.

phenocryst A relatively large crystal in a *porphyritic* rock.

physiography The descriptive study of land forms.

plug A vertical *igneous* pipe, the channel by which *magma* reached a *volcanic vent.*

pluton An *igneous intrusion* formed at depth, of area greater than 40 square miles and with no known floor.

porphyritic Describes a rock in which larger crystals are set in a finer grained *groundmass.*

pyroclastic flow A flow of *pyroclastic* particles, usually very hot; synonymous with *ash flow*.

pyroclastic surge deposit A stratified layer of *pyroclasts* left by a cloud of hot particles and gas moving turbulently along the ground from a volcanic vent.

pyroclast An individual particle of rock ejected by an explosive volcanic eruption; from the Ancient Greek words for *fire* and *broken into pieces*; the adjective is **pyroclastic**.

rhyolite A group of fine-grained *extrusive* rocks, typically *porphyritic* and commonly exhibiting flow structures, with *phenocrysts* of quartz and *alkali feldspar* in a glassy to *cryptocrystalline groundmass*, the fine-grained equivalent of *granite*. Rhyolite grades into *trachyte* with a decrease in quartz content.

sediment Fragments that originate by weathering of older rocks and forms in layers on the Earth's surface as sand, gravel, silt, mud etc.

sedimentary rock A rock that has formed from the consolidation of loose sediment such as fragments of older rock, chemically precipitated material, volcanic pyroclastic fragments, and organic remains.

sill A broad, tabular *igneous intrusion* that parallels the bedding or foliation of the rock into which it was intruded.

stock An *igneous intrusion* formed at depth of area 40 square miles or less and with no known floor.

syenite A group of *plutonic* rocks containing *alkali feldspar*, plagioclase, one or more *mafic* minerals, with quartz, if present, only as an accessory; the intrusive equivalent of *trachyte*; with increasing quartz, grades into *granite*.

syncline A fold, generally concave up, whose core contains younger rocks..

synclinorium A broad syncline extending over a large area on which is superimposed minor folds.

thrust fault A fault where the upper or hanging wall has moved over the lower or foot wall, shortening the earth's crust.

trachyte A group of fine-grained *extrusive* rocks, generally *porphyritic*, having *alkali feldspar* and minor *mafic* minerals as the main components, the *extrusive* equivalent of *syenite*. *Trachyte* grades into *rhyolite* as the quartz content increases.

tuff A rock composed of consolidated or cemented volcanic ash; includes *ash-flow tuff* and *ash-fall tuff.*

volcanic breccia A *volcaniclastic* rock composed mainly of volcanic fragments greater than 2 mm in diameter.

volcanic neck The volcanic rock filling the vent of an extinct volcano.

volcaniclastic Pertaining to a *sedimentary* rock composed of mainly or partly of broken fragments of volcanic origin.

welded tuff A rock composed of *pyroclasts* welded together by a combination of heat of the particles, the weight of overlying material and hot gases.

Reading List

Barker, D.S., Henry, C.D. and Mcdowell, F.W., 1986, Pine Canyon Caldera, Big Bend National Park, a mildly peralkaline magmatic system *in* Price, J.G., Henry, C.D., Parker, D.F. and Barker, D.S., eds., Igneous geology of Trans-Pecos Texas: University of Texas at Austin, Bureau of Economic Geology Guidebook No. 23, p.266-85.

Barker, D.S., 2000, Down to Earth at Tuff Canyon, Big Bend National Park, Texas: University of Texas at Austin, Bureau of Economic Geology Guidebook , 40 p.

Barnes V.E., Project Director, 1982, Fort Stockton Sheet, *in* Geological Atlas of Texas: The University of Texas at Austin, Bureau of Economic Geology, scale 1:250,000.

Barnes V.E., Project Director, 1979, Emory Peak-Presidio Sheet, *in* Geological Atlas of Texas: The University of Texas at Austin, Bureau of Economic Geology, scale 1:250,000.

Casey, C.B., 1972, Mirages, mysteries and reality, Brewster County Texas. The Big Bend of the Rio Grande: Pioneer Book Publishers, 1972.

Casey, C.B., 1969, Soldiers, ranchers and miners in the Big Bend: U.S. National Park Service, Division of History, Office of Archeology and Historic Preservation, Washington, 267 p.

Cobb, R.C., and Poth, S., 1980, Superimposed deformation in the Santiago and northern Del Carmen Mountains, Trans-Pecos: New Mexico Geological Society Guidebook, 31st Field Conference, Trans-Pecos Region, p.71-5.

Collinson, F., 1963, Life in the Saddle: University of Oklahoma Press, Norman, Oklahoma, 241 p.

Collinsworth, B.C., and Rohr, D.M., 1986, An Eocene carbonate lacustrine deposit, Brewster County, West Texas *in* Pause, P.H. and Spears, R. G., eds., Geology of the Big Bend and Solitario Dome: West Texas Geological Society 1986 Field Trip Guidebook, p.117-24.

Dahl, D.A, and Lambert, D.D., 1986, Petrology of the Black Hills, Brewster County, Texas, *in* Price, J.G., Henry, C.D. Parker, D.F., Jr., and Barker, D. S. eds., Igneous geology of Trans-Pecos Texas: Texas Bureau of Economic Geology, Guidebook 23, p.320-32.

Deal, D., 1979, Evolution of the Rio Conchos-Rio Grande drainage system *in* Walton, A.W., and Henry, C.D., eds., Cenozoic Geology of the Trans-Pecos volcanic field of Texas: Texas Bureau of Economic Geology, Guidebook 19, p.137-47.

DeCamp, D. W., 1985, Structural geology of Mesa de Anguila, Big Bend National Park *in* Dickerson P.W., and Muehlberger, W.R., eds., Structure and tectonics of Trans-Pecos Texas: West Texas Geological Society Field Conference 1985 p.127-136.

Dickerson, P.W., and Muehlberger, W.R., 1994, Basins in the Big Bend segment, Rio Grande rift *in* Keller G.R., and Cather S.M., eds., Basins of the Rio Grande rift : structure, stratigraphy, and tectonic setting: Geological Society of America Special Paper No 291 p.283-297.

Eifler, G.K., Jr., 1943, Geology of the Santiago Peak Quadrangle, Texas: Geological Society of America Bulletin, v.43, p.1613-44.

Erdlac, R.J., Jr., 1990, A Laramide push-up block: Structures and formation of Terlingua-Solitario structural block, Big Bend region, Texas: Geological Society of America Bulletin v.102, p.1065-76.

Erickson, R.L., 1953, Stratigraphy and petrology of the Tascotal Mesa Quadrangle, Texas: Geological Society of America Bulletin v. 64 p.1353-86.

Goldich, S.S., and Elms, M.A., 1946, Stratigraphy and petrography of the Buck Hill Quadrangle, Texas: Geological Society of America Bulletin, v.60, p. 1133-83.

Graves, R.W., Jr., Geology of Hood Spring Quadrangle, Brewster County, Texas: Bureau of Economic Geology Report of Investigations No. 21, 51 p.

Henry, C.D., Kunk, M.J. and McIntosh, W.C., 1994, 40Ar/39Ar chronology and volcanology of silicic volcanism in the Davis Mountains, Trans-Pecos Texas: Geological Society of America Bulletin v. 106 p.1359-76.

Henry, C.D., 1998, Geology of Big Bend Ranch State Park: The University of Texas at Austin, Bureau of Economic Geology Guidebook 27, 72 p.

Henry, C.D., Gluck, J.K., and Bockoven, N.T., 1985, Tectonic map of the Basin and Range Province of Texas and adjacent Mexico: The University of Texas at Austin, Bureau of Economic Geology Miscellaneous Map No. 36.

Henry, C.D, Price, J.G., and Miser, D.E., 1989, Geology and Tertiary igneous activity of the Hen Egg Mountain and Christmas Mountain Quadrangles, Big-Bend Region, Trans-Pecos Texas: Bureau of Economic Geology Report of Investigations No. 183, 105 p.

Henry, C.D. and McDowell, F.W., 1986, Geochronology of magmatism in the Tertiary volcanic field, Trans-Pecos Texas *in* Price, J.G., Henry, C.D., Parker, D.F. and Barker, D.S., eds., Igneous geology of Trans-Pecos Texas: The University of Texas at Austin, Bureau of Economic Geology Guidebook No. 23, p. 99-122.

Jons, R.D., 1981, ed. Marathon-Marfa region of West Texas: Society of Economic Paleontologists and Mineralogists, Permian Basin Section, Publication 81-20, 226 p.

King, P.B., 1930, The geology of the Glass Mountains, Texas: Part 1, Stratigraphy: The University of Texas at Austin, The University of Texas Bulletin 3038, 167 p.

King, P.B., 1937, The geology of the Marathon region Texas: United States Geological Survey Professional Paper 187, 148 p.

King, P.B., 1980, Geology of the Eastern Part of the Marathon Basin, Texas: United States Geological Survey Professional Paper 1157, 40p.

Langford, J.O. with Fred Gipson, *Big Bend: A Homesteader's Story*: Austin, University of Texas Press, 1952.

Lehman, T.M., 1986, Late Cretaceous sedimentation in Trans-Pecos Texas: West Texas Geological Society Publication 8682, p.35-54.

Lehman, T.M., 1990, Paleosols and the Cretaceous/Tertiary transition in the Big Bend Region of Texas: Geology, v.18, p.362-4.

Lehman, T.M., 1991, Sedimentation and tectonism in the Laramide Tornillo Basin of West Texas: Sedimentary Geology, v.75, p.9-28.

Lonsdale, J.T., 1940, Igneous rocks of the Terlingua-Solitario region, Texas: Geological Society of America, v. 51, p.1539-1626.

Madison, V.D. and Stillwell H.C., *How Come It's Called That?*: Marathon, Texas, Iron Mountain Press, 1997.

Maler, M.O., 1990, Dead Horse Graben; a West Texas accommodation zone: Tectonics, v. 9, p.1357-68.

Maxwell, R.A., 1968, The Big Bend of the Rio Grande: University of Texas at Austin, Bureau of Economic Geology Guidebook 7, 138 p.

Maxwell, R.A., Lonsdale, J.T., Hazzard, R.T., and Wilson, J.A., 1967, Geology of Big Bend National Park, Brewster County, Texas: University of Texas, Bureau of Economic Geology Publication No. 6711, 320 p.

McAnulty, W.N., 1955, Geology of Cathedral Mountain Quadrangle, Brewster County, Texas: Geological Society of America Bulletin, v.66, p.531-78.

McAnulty, W.N., 1950, Geology and ground-water resources of Alpine and adjacent territory, Brewster County, Texas: Unpublished manuscript.

McBride, E.F., 1978, Tesnus and Haymond Formations – Siliclastic Flysch *in* Mazzullo, S.J. ed. Tectonics and Paleozoic Facies of the Marathon Geosyncline West Texas: Society of Economic Paleontologists and Mineralogists, Permian Basin Section, Publication 78-17, p.131-48.

McBride, E.F., 1989, Stratigraphy and structure of Marathon Region, West Texas, *in* Muehlberger, W.R. and Dickerson, P.W. eds. Structure and stratigraphy of Trans-Pecos Texas: 28th International Geological Congress, Field Trip Guidebook T317, p.147-54.

Moon. C.G., 1953, Geology of the Aqua Fria Quadrangle, Brewster County, Texas: Geological Society of America Bulletin, v.64, p.151-95.

Muehlberger, W.R., 1989, Summary of the structural geology of Big Bend National Park and vicinity *in* Muehlberger, W.R. and Dickerson, P.W. eds. Structure and stratigraphy of Trans-Pecos Texas: 28th International Geological Congress, Field Trip Guidebook T317, p.179-97.

Musgrove, M., Banner, J.L., Mack, L.E., Combs, D.M. and James, E.W., 2001, Geochronology of late Pleistocene to Holocene speleothems from Central Texas: Implications for regional paleoclimate: Geological Society of America Bulletin, v.113, no.2: p. 1532-43.

Nelson, K.L., 1992, A road guide to the geology of Big Bend National Park: Big Bend Natural History Association, 76 p.

Nelson, D.O. and Nelson, K.L., 1986, Supplementary road log – Alpine-Fort Davis-Davis mountain loop *in* Pause, P.H. and Spears, R. G. eds., Geology of the Big Bend and Solitario Dome: West Texas Geological Society 1986 Field Trip Guidebook, pp. 63-73.

Ogley, D.S., 1979, Eruptive history of the Pine Canyon Caldera, Big Bend National Park, *in* Walton, A.W., and Henry, C.D., eds., Cenozoic geology of the Trans-Pecos volcanic field of Texas: University of Texas at Austin, Bureau of Economic Geology, Guidebook 19, p. 67-71.

Palczynsky, C.E.P., 2001, Groundwater in the Tertiary volcanic sequence of the Eastern Davis Mountains, Trans-Pecos Texas (M.S. Thesis): Alpine, Texas, Sul Ross State University, 158p.

Parent, L., 1996, *Hiking the Big Bend National Park*: Falcon Publishing, Helena, Montana 171 p.

Parker, D.F., and McDowell, F.W., 1979, K-Ar geochronology of Oligocene volcanic rocks, Davis and Barilla Mountains, Texas: Geological Society of America Bulletin, v.90, p.1100-10.

Parker, D.F., 1979a, The Paisano Volcano: Stratigraphy, age, and petrogenesis *in* Walton, A.W., and Henry, C.D., eds., Cenozoic geology of the Trans-Pecos volcanic field of Texas: University of Texas at Austin, Bureau of Economic Geology, Guidebook 19, 193 p., p. 97-105.

Parker, D.F., 1979b, The Paisano Volcano: Field Trip Stops *in* Walton, A.W., and Henry, C.D., eds., Cenozoic geology of the Trans-Pecos volcanic field of Texas: University of Texas at Austin, Bureau of Economic Geology, Guidebook 19, 193 p.

Parker, D.F., 2002, Horseshoe Canyon Volcanic Dome *in* White, J.C. ed., The geology of Big Bend National Park: What we have learned since Maxwell and others (1967)?: Geological Society of America Field Trip Guide, p. 24-32.

Pearson, B.T., 1978, Ouachita-Marathon geosynclinal facies in the Green Valley area, Brewster County, Texas, *in* Mazzullo, S.J. ed., Tectonics and Paleozoic facies of the Marathon geosyncline, West Texas: Society of Economic Paleontologists and Mineralogists, Permian Basin Section, Field Conference Guidebook, p.95-100.

Pearson, B.T., 1981, Some structural problems of the Marfa Basin area, *in* Johns, R.D ed., Marathon-Marfa region of West Texas: Society of Economic Paleontologists and Mineralogists, Permian Basin Section, Publication 81-20, p.59-73.

Price, J.G., Henry, C.D., Parker, D.F. and Barker, D.S., 1986 eds. Igneous Geology of Trans-Pecos Texas: University of Texas at Austin, Bureau of Economic Geology, Guidebook 23, 360 p.

Ragsdale, K.B. *Quicksilver: Terlingua & the Chisos Mining Company*: College Station, Texas A & M University Press, 1976.

Stevens, J.B., and Stevens, M.S., 1990a, Stratigraphy and major structural-tectonic events along and near the Rio Grande, Trans-Pecos Texas and adjacent Chihuahua and Coahuila, Mexico *in* Dickerson, P.W., Stevens, M.S., and Stevens, J.B., eds., Geology of the Big Bend and Trans-Pecos region: South Texas Geological Society, 1989 Annual Meeting of the American Association of Petroleum Geologists, Field Trip Guidebook, p.73-116.

Stevens, J.B., and Stevens, M.S., 1990b, Road logs, field trip to Big Bend region, Trans-Pecos Texas in Dickerson, P.W., Stevens, M.S., and Stevens, J.B., eds., Geology of the Big Bend and Trans-Pecos region: South Texas Geological Society, 1989 Annual Meeting of the American Association of Petroleum Geologists, Field Trip Guidebook, p.1-72.

St. John, B.E., 1965, Geology of Black Gap area, Brewster County, Texas: Texas Bureau of Economic Geology, Geological Quadrangle Map No. 30, Scale 1:62,500.

Smith, C.I., 1970, Lower Cretaceous Stratigraphy, Northern Coahuila, Mexico: University of Texas at Austin, Bureau of Economic Geology, Report of Investigations No. 65, 101 p.

Spearing, D., 1991, Roadside geology of Texas: Mountain Press Publishing Company, Missoula, Montana, 418 p.

Tauvers, P.R. and Muehlberger, W.R., 1989a, Structural styles in the western domain of the Marathon Basin, Trans-Pecos, Texas *in* Muehlberger, W.R., and Dickerson, P.W., eds., Structure and stratigraphy of Trans-Pecos Texas: 28th International Geological Congress, Field Trip Guidebook T317, p.155-70.

Tauvers, P.R., and Muehlberger, W.R., 1989b, Persimmon Gap in Big Bend National Park, Texas; Ouachita facies and Cretaceous cover deformed in a Laramide overthrust *in* Muehlberger, W.R., and Dickerson, P.W., eds., Structure and stratigraphy of Trans-Pecos Texas: 28th International Geological Congress, Field Trip Guidebook T317, p.171-77.

Udden, J.A., 1907, A sketch of the geology of the Chisos country, Brewster County, Texas: The University of Texas Bulletin 93, 101 p.

Walton, A.W., 1979, Sedimentology and diagenesis of the Tascotal Formation, a brief summary, *in* Walton, A.W., and Henry, C.D., eds., Cenozoic geology of the Trans-Pecos volcanic field of Texas: University of Texas at Austin, Bureau of Economic Geology, Guidebook 19, p.157-61.

Wermund, E.G., 1996, Physiograpic map of Texas: The University of Texas at Austin, Bureau of Economic Geology.

Wilcox, Robert B., 1989, Evidence for an early Cretaceous age for the Bissett Formation, western Glass Mountains, Brewster and Pecos Counties, West Texas: implications for regional stratigraphy, paleogeography, and tectonics: Alpine, Texas, Sul Ross State University, Masters Thesis, 253 p.

Wilshire, H.G., Offield, T.W., Howard, K.A., and Cummings, D., 1972, Geology of the Sierra Madera Cryptoexplosion structure, Pecos county, Texas: U.S. Geological Survey Professional Paper 599H, 42 p.

Winograd, I.J., Coplen, T.B., Landwehr, J.M., Riggs, A.C., Ludwig, K.R., Szabo, B.J., Kolesar, P.T., and Revesz, K.M., 1992, Continuous 500,000-Year Climate Record from Vein Calcite in Devils Hole, Nevada: Science, v.258, p.255-60.

Woodward, T.R., 1981, Bird Mine, Brewster County, Texas: in Jons, R.D., ed., Marathon-Marfa region of West Texas: Society of Economic Paleontologists and Mineralogists, Permian Basin Section, Publication 81-20, p. 225-7.

Yates, R.B, and Thompson, G.A., 1959, Geology and quicksilver deposits of the Terlingua District, Texas: U.S. Geological Survey Professional Paper 312, 114 p.

Index